Jean-Marie Ballu

C000280665

La Fayette's liberty ship of 1780

The reconstruction of the frigate *Hermione*

Éditions du Gerfaut

Translated from French by David Karslake

Thanks

The Association Hermione La Fayette
The Service Historique de la Marine
The Marine Nationale and the Office National des Forêts
All those who have taken part in this adventure and particularly :
Alexandre Genoud, shipwright
Anne Renaud, sail maker
Gérard Bernard, expert and shipwright working for the Bernard shipyard at St. Vaast La Hougue (managed by Gilles Auger)
François Asselin and Jacques Haie of the Asselin company
Jean Boudriot, naval historian
Emmanuel de Fontainieu, of the Corderie et Centre International de la Mer at Rochefort
Jean-Luc Gireaud and Robert Kalbach, authors of *L'Hermione, frégate des lumières*
Jean Thomas, historian, cabinetmaker, model maker and great expert on the *Hermione*
Maryse Vital, Isabelle Georget and Stéphane Munari of the Association Hermione La Fayette and Benedict Donnelly

Lastly :
The Musée Nationale de la Marine in Paris, Brest and Rochefort and its archives and photography department
The Corderie Royale de Rochefort

Illustrations

The photographs captioned '*photos AH*' are those reproduced by kind permission of the Association Hermione La Fayette. Photos captioned '*photos AH SM*' were taken by Stéphane Munari for the association.
All drawings and photographs for which no source is given are those of the author.
The sources of illustrations are shown at the end of the captions.

Title page :
The Marquis de La Fayette, wearing the uniform of a caption of the de Noailles regiment, during the period in which he embarked on the Hermione to go to the United States. Painting by Louis-Léopold Boilly, in the museum of Versailles and the Trianon. © Réunion des musées nationaux, Gérard Blot.

Contents

Brest, 1996. The HMS Rose, an American replica of an English frigate which took part in the American War of Independence. Although considerably smaller than the Hermione, this ship looks much like her, being of similar date and construction. Photo Loïc Le Moyne.

Chapter I

Why reconstruct the *Hermione* ?

Prelude

An exhibition shipyard

What an extraordinary challenge to try to build a replica of a ship of such a size in an *exhibition shipyard* in order to explain shipbuilding in the reign of Louis XVI, to enable the public to witness the stages of the construction of a 12 pounder[1] frigate and to bring to life again the adventure of La Fayette !

1/36ᵗʰ scale model of the Hermione, *made by Jean-Claude Cossais, showing her 12 and 6 pdr guns.*

Is this not anachronistic, even a bit archaic ? What is the point of building in the 21ˢᵗ century a frigate of the 18ᵗʰ century ? The hundreds of thousands of visitors who come every year to share the enthusiasm for this project give the answer and they are right ! They recognize a beautiful creation that transcends our everyday lives !

---

[1] Pounder, normally abbreviated to pdr, indicates the calibre of gun carried, expressed as the weight of shot fired.

This work of solid oak will surely be a floating piece of monumental sculpture. What emotion already emanates from this work of art fit to be a museum exhibit by its period and its authenticity ! It is not a matter of sterile nostalgia to go back to our roots and to show our maritime heritage.

What a magnificent objective to want to make an authentic 18th century ship go to sea. It is also highly moving to find once more forgotten know-how and lost manual skills, to plunge into the past by attempting to reproduce the experiences of our forebears, extraordinary shipbuilders that they were. Such a dive into history makes us dream of a world in which crossing the Atlantic took a month and a half of perilous navigation, of a time when France wanted to help America and to believe in the hope of universal liberty !

We must thank those who have enabled us to pass from this daydreaming to a real-life experience.

Is it detrimental to the forest to use wood for shipbuilding? No.

The glass, iron and salt industries between them consumed huge quantities of wood to provide the energy for all their factories. Over the centuries, navies also drew heavily on the world's forests and much of this wood ended up at the bottom of the oceans. France was an exception, thanks to the intuition of its kings, and today it still has a rich and extensive expanse of forest, whereas in other countries the needs of shipbuilding have caused the forests to be hacked down and be replaced by deserts.

Forests in France are today more widespread and well-stocked than they have been in any previous period and their surface is double what it was just after the Revolution. The tree, a living being, naturally has a limited life span. For the forest to endure, it must be constantly renewed and rejuvenated.

Using wood is helping the planet, because the photosynthesis of trees absorbs CO_2, releases oxygen and makes new wood. Only a properly managed forest, which exploits its resources of wood, can be a green lung for the planet. To combat the "greenhouse effect", the forest must produce wood.

So let us build everything we can from wood !

SHIPBUILDING IN FRANCE

In the 1990s, shipbuilding only used 8 000 m³ of oak per year, a mere drop in the ocean of the volume available !

The volume of standing oak in French forests is 525 million m³ and the amount cut annually is 17 million m³. The forests in France are substantially under-exploited, the wood cut every year being hardly more than half of the annual biological production.

France could today supply wood to build Louis XVI's great fleet ten times over.

As for the Hermione, she will need 1 160 m³ of oak and 205 m³ of coniferous trees. As her construction will be spread over about fifteen years, the annual volume is less than 100 m³, which is insignificant, being approximately 1/200 000th of annual output !

The birth of Rochefort

Where to build a military port ? La Roche-Bernard

Richelieu had already decided, in 1629, to build the Couronne, the prototype of a future series of line of battle vessels, at La Roche Bernard, a hidden port 16 km inland in a steep-sided and easily defendable valley. This ship, which was very large for the period, 66m long with 72 gun ports, marks the true birth of the French fleet and heralded the construction of the naval dockyards of Toulon, Brest and Rochefort.

For the construction of warships, it was necessary to have a large dockyard, well protected against the English enemy. Brest, chosen by Richelieu but built by Colbert from 1670 onwards, is hidden away at the far end of a large natural harbour and is protected by a narrows with powerful gun batteries. The enemy fleet cannot get inside, but can easily maintain a blockade to stop the French ships getting out, owing to the closeness of the English coast.

The king wanted to build another dockyard farther away from the British Isles and in 1666 chose Rochefort[2], concealed inland, after ruling out the port of La Rochelle, a Protestant stronghold.

The birth of the naval dockyard at Rochefort, the Versailles of the sea

Colbert[3] obeyed the instructions of the king to build "rapid, beautiful and large".

Model of the port and dockyard of Rochefort, made by the Centre International de la Mer at Rochefort.

Like Versailles, it cost so much that Louis XIV is said to have exclaimed "Rochefort is certainly paved with gold !"

Colossal sums were swallowed up in consolidating the unstable ground. Rochefort was a small island in the marshes of the mouth of the Charente river and it was on it that Colbert de Terron[4] founded the dockyard and the town. The rope factory, the forge for bronze canons and the anchor park were begun in 1666 and the great warehouses, including the gunpowder store and the mast and spar shed, followed in 1668. These were handsome monuments but also a real factory which would launch 550 warships.

---

[2] See the thesis of Martine Acerra. The navy closed the Rochefort dockyard in 1927.
[3] Jean-Baptiste Colbert, Finance Minister in 1661 and of the Navy in 1669, became the Marquess of Seignelay.
[4] Cousin of Jean-Baptiste Colbert, the minister, and Governor of Brouage.

The Admiral's Fountain, no longer vertical because of the unstable ground. On the left the Admiral's Guardhouse and to the right the rope factory, occupied today by the Centre International de la Mer.

FROM ROCHEFORT TO THE OCEAN

Well protected and guarded at the sea entrance by the forts on the islands of Aix, Oléron and Madame, this inland dockyard could only be reached at high tide and by nothing larger than a 74-gun ship. As the size of vessels grew, only frigates and corvettes could get to Rochefort, which thus lost most of its usefulness[5]. The Charente, with a draught of seven metres and a winding course, could not be navigated under

The port of Rochefort, watercolour dated 1820 by Ballon de Compiègne. Musée national de la Marine à Paris, photo Dantec.

Left hand side : the Hermione was probably built in one of these 4 roofed slipways.
In the centre, a masting sheer-hulk and in the foreground a gang of convicts hauling a frigate upstream along the Charente. Another gang going down river can be seen on the right.
On the right, the windmill of the sawmill.

[5] According to the specialist Martine Acerra, the output of the Rochefort dockyard amounted in its heyday to nearly a third of the fleet but fell sharply in the 18th century to only 15%.

The first graving dock, to a design by Clerville, was built from May 1669 to July 1671. When this became inadequate, a double dock , designed by Pierre Arnoul, was started in 1683. The construction was made difficult by resurgences. Because of lack of space, many buildings, including the very long rope factory, had been put up on marshy ground on an artificial apron which was virtually a floating raft. Large numbers of oak trees were used to make these foundation platforms and support structures before the first ships were built.

The dockyard was closed in 1927 and Rochefort declined. Starting in 1974, the town launched projects in aeronautics, national heritage and tourism. A cultural initiative was the creation of the Centre International de la Mer, housed in the renovated rope factory. The oldest dry dock was cleared of silt in 1985 and the double dock was excavated from 1992 onwards. On the 4th of July 1997 the keel of the Hermione began to be assembled there.

sail. The ships, with their ballast and armament removed, were towed by teams of men. Small boats took ammunition and other supplies downstream to the ships waiting in the Aix roadstead, where they were armed and loaded. The banks of the Charente were fitted out with stakes or, after 1722, with discarded canons, which allowed the vessels to be towed upstream or downstream along the 22 km distance and to be moored. The inhabitants of the neighbouring villages had to perform this forced labour until they were replaced by convicts in 1766.

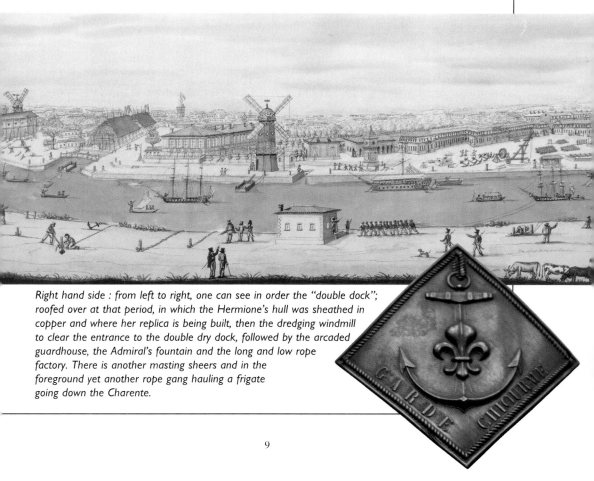

Right hand side : from left to right, one can see in order the "double dock"; roofed over at that period, in which the Hermione's hull was sheathed in copper and where her replica is being built, then the dredging windmill to clear the entrance to the double dry dock, followed by the arcaded guardhouse, the Admiral's fountain and the long and low rope factory. There is another masting sheers and in the foreground yet another rope gang hauling a frigate going down the Charente.

From the French colonies in America to American independence

The Seven Years' War and the French loss of its American colonies

France, having lost the war (1756-1763), signed the disastrous Treaty of Paris on February 10th 1763 and gave up "New France". Consequently, France would wait for her hour of revenge and England would ruin herself maintaining an army to keep control of the colonies. With the Treasury empty, London imposed new taxes on the thirteen colonies of New England[6].

Mounting tension : Indians, English taxes and the Tea war

In New England, incidents, often serious ones, multiplied between the Crown and the colonists, who found it increasingly hard to put up with the ever harsher regime of the authorities.

In 1773, new taxes were introduced on iron, paper and tea. The Tea Act particularly angered the settlers, who boycotted English products. During the night of December 16th, colonists disguised as Indians boarded three ships laden with tea in Boston harbour and threw 340 cases into the sea. After this Boston Tea party, the British government closed the port of Boston until the destroyed cargo had been paid for. 12 000 soldiers were sent to restore law and order.

On September 15th 1774, the First Continental Congress met in Philadelphia and Benjamin Franklin prepared a declaration of rights stating that no British citizen should be taxed without his consent. King George did not have the same point of view and thought that "the colonies must submit or triumph".

1775 The start of the war

To put down the rebellion, which was growing and becoming more organized, The Royal Navy landed 40 000 soldiers in New Jersey.

The Congress[7] in Philadelphia in its turn raised the Continental Army and gave its command to George Washington. It consisted of loosely organized and badly equipped groups of militia, initially using skirmishing and sniping tactics. The Congress also decided to create a Navy Committee, later to become a ministry, and the Continental Navy. It sought the support of France and on the 4th of July 1776[8] voted the Declaration of Independence of the United States of America[9]. The next day the New Yorkers pulled down the lead statue of the king and made 42 000 musket-balls out of it.

---

[6] *Massachusetts, New Hampshire, Rhode Island, Connecticut, New York, New Jersey, Pennsylvania, Delaware, Maryland, Virginia, South Carolina and Georgia.*
[7] Second Continental Congress.
[8] *Independance Day.* The American flag was to be created by an act of June 14th 1777, with 13 alternate red and white stripes and a blue square with 13 stars representing the founding colonies. The numbers would increase with each additional state, the 50th being in 1960.
[9] Right to be free and independent states, based on the three pillars of life, liberty and happiness.

After Saratoga, France officially enters the conflict in 1778

After two difficult years, General Burgoyne, finding himself surrounded on October 17th 1777, surrendered near Saratoga. This was the first major victory for the rebels. As the American cause was very popular in France, a treaty of alliance was signed in Paris on February 6th 1778. After France declared war on Britain that summer, the United States disposed of French military and naval resources.

Sea and land victories : Chesapeake Bay and Yorktown

As the allies became bogged down besieging New York, where the British were supplied by their navy, the war took a decisive turn with the arrival of 38 ships of Admiral de Grasse's squadron, which La Fayette had begged Vergennes, the Foreign Affairs Minister, to send.

Washington wanted to take New York, but de Grasse and General de Rochambeau, commander of the French expeditionary force, chose Chesapeake Bay, because General Cornwallis with his tired army, harried by La Fayette, had retired to a base on the shore of the York River. The troops of de Rochambeau and Washington made a forced march of 800 km in gruelling conditions to join up with La Fayette's force. Cornwallis found himself trapped at Yorktown and Admiral de Grasse got there on August 30 and landed reinforcements.

The French naval victory of Chesapeake on September 5th 1781 prevented the Royal Navy from coming to the rescue of the British army surrounded at Yorktown. After unsuccessful attempts to break out and having had to face a last attack led by the 24 year old La Fayette, Cornwallis surrendered on October 19th.

The defeat of the army led the British parliament to recognize the independence of the 13 colonies and the war was ended by the Treaty of Versailles signed on September 3rd 1783. It brought France very little other than prestige… and huge financial difficulties, which were one of the causes of the convocation of the States General in 1789 and this in turn heralded the French Revolution.

George Washington, soon to be the first President of the United States, acknowledged that without French help, the Americans would have been "drowned in blood" and he expressed "the undying gratitude of every American citizen towards France."

A preparatory stop at Saint-Domingue. Arriving on 15th April 1781, de Grasse's squadron, at the request of de Rochambeau, embarked 3000 soldiers and canons from the French garrison. These were landed at Chesapeake on August 30th, before the squadron set sail at once for the major naval battle of Chesapeake Bay on September 5th. This led directly to the land victory at Yorktown on October 17th. Painting by Gustave Alaux (1887-1965).
Photo Musée National de la Marine, Paris

Meeting between de Grasse, de Rochambeau and Washington on the flagship Ville de Paris *on 17th September 1781 to discuss the forthcoming attack.*
Musée national de la Marine d'après Charles Cerny.

The French Navy, key to the victory

In the wake of the decisions taken by Louis XVI, the French Navy had finally become powerful. The Royal Navy was obliged to disperse its forces in the Channel, the Atlantic and the Indian colonies The possibility of a French invasion, with 40 000 men gathered in Normandy in 1778 and 1779, prevented it from reducing the defensive coverage of the English coasts and from keeping a close watch on the port of Brest, as it had done during the Seven Years' War. An adequate watch over the American coasts was impossible, owing to the great number and depth of the river estuaries, such as the tributaries of the Chesapeake, in which frigates could navigate. Even the war on land was dependent on the Navy, as supplies and reinforcements for both sides were brought in via the ports and rivers.

Through the control of ports, the transport of reinforcements and the naval battles, the French Navy, with its 123 vessels provided the key to Independence.

Battle between squadrons at Chesapeake Bay on 5th September 1781, by A.M.Zweg
Navy Museum in Washington. Photo Musée National de la Marine, Paris.

What did La Fayette go to do in America ?

The first voyage

Marie-Joseph Gilbert Motier, Marquis de La Fayette (1757-1834) inherited at the age of 13 his father's large fortune. As a 17 year old sub-lieutenant, he was enthusiastic about the new philosophical ideas. He was much taken with Benjamin Franklin, then on a mission to Paris, 70 years old and hardly speaking any French. He was later to say "my heart had been enrolled by the Declaration of Independence". In spite of the opposition of the government, which forbade any French officer to serve in the North American colonies, and that of his father-in-law, the Duc de Noailles, who wanted to have him locked up in the Bastille prison, he enlisted and had to hide. France was not yet ready for war and its fleet was still insufficient. Any French "aggression" would put its alliances at risk. Secretly, but probably with the tacit agreement of

The Marquis de La Fayette in America. Musée Carnavalet, Paris ; Réunion des musées nationaux, © Bulloz.

the king, he bought a ship, *La Victoire*, (see painting on Page 136) and on the 20th of April 1777 he left Bordeaux to go to America to help the insurgents. He landed at Georgetown and wrote to his wife "I have come here without permission, without any approval other than silence." His enthusiasm quickly worked wonders and he met Washington, a fellow freemason. Almost on his twentieth birthday, a bullet wounded him in the thigh and Washington ordered that he should be cared for as if he was his son. He was put in command of 2 000 men and his brilliant handling of several actions crowned him with a glory that was recognized by the Congress.

The second voyage, with the *Hermione*

To convince Louis XVI to come to the help of the rebels, La Fayette left Boston on 11th January 1779 aboard the *Alliance*, an American frigate with a French captain. He reached Brest on February 6th and hastened to Versailles where he was successful in his mission. He returned to Rochefort, embarked on the *Hermione* on 10th March 1780 and got back to Boston on April 27th to announce the arrival of a contingent commanded, much to his own disappointment, by the very diligent General de Rochambeau. After Yorktown, he left America in December 1781, covered in honours and returned wreathed in glory to France, where he was promoted to the rank of Brigadier.

He subsequently had a chequered political career. A hero of the beginning of the Revolution, he was later declared a traitor of the nation and had to flee the country[10]. After a period vegetating in the depths of his country estates, he made a further voyage to the United States in 1824 -1825, where he was given a triumphant welcome, before becoming one of the major protagonists in the accession of Louis-Philippe in 1830.

[10] He was arrested at Rochefort (in Belgium) by the Austrians and imprisoned.

The American campaigns of the *Hermione*

The *Hermione* was one of the vessels built during the renaissance of the French fleet at the behest of Louis XVI. Commanded by Louis-René de la Touche[11], a 22 year old lieutenant, she took to sea in May 1779 and captured three English privateers and three merchant ships in the Atlantic. She then returned in November 1779 to the Rochefort dry dock to have her hull sheathed in copper to improve her speed.

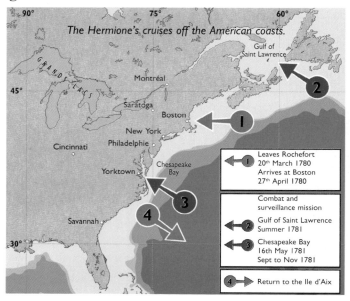

The *Hermione's* cruises off the American coasts.

	Leaves Rochefort 20th March 1780 Arrives at Boston 27th April 1780
	Combat and surveillance mission
	Gulf of Saint Lawrence Summer 1781
	Chesapeake Bay 16th May 1781 Sept to Nov 1781
	Return to the Ile d'Aix

At Port-des-Barques, La Touche was waiting with a crew of 330 sailors and supplies for six months stowed on the frigate, ready to set sail for America on a secret mission[12]. On 10th March 1780 appeared "Monsieur le Marquis de La Fayette, Colonel of the King's regiment, dragoon and general major in the service of the United States of America", accompanied by his secretary, two officers and his servants. The *Hermione* cast off on March 20th, "avoiding any sails that she might come across" according to strict orders, crossed the Atlantic in 38 days and put into Boston. While La Fayette went off to join Washington, the *Hermione* received an enthusiastic welcome from the Americans and the elected representatives of Massachusetts came aboard for a visit. For the next two years she participated in the protection of the coasts and the capture of British merchant ships. On 7th June 1780 she was victorious in an engagement against the British frigate *Iris*. During the summer of 1781, the *Hermione* and the *Astrée*, commanded by La Pérouse cruised together in the Gulf of Saint Lawrence and captured many prizes.

The *Hermione* joined the French squadron after de Rochambeau's landing in July 1780 to defend Newport. Then in May 1781 she took part in a first battle at the entrance of the bay and finally in the battle between squadrons in Chesapeake Bay from September until November 1781.

The squadron under Admiral de Grasse set sail on November 4th to go to La Martinique, but the *Hermione* remained under the orders of General de Rochambeau until leaving on 2nd February 1782 to return to the Ile d'Aix.

Between 10th March 1780 and 25th February 1782, the *Hermione* captured 9 enemy ships and sustained 44 deaths, of which 17 occurred in battle, and 53 wounded.

---

[11] He had first seen action at the age of 13 at the battle of the Cardinals.

[12] Letter dated 6th March 1780 from the minister Sartine *"For your eyes only* (top secret). *Mr de La Fayette should inform you of the names of the four officers and the eight domestic servants who are to accompany him on the Hermione. The intention of the King is that on no account are any other passengers to be taken on board."*

The Hermione *on the left at the Battle of Louisburg on 21ˢᵗ July 1781 against six British ships, during which she fired 509 canon shots. Detail of an oil painting on canvas by Auguste Louis de Rossel de Cercy 1788.*
Musée national de la Marine à Rochefort, photo studio Laurent.

THE SOCIETY OF THE CINCINNATI[13]

The American officers wanted, as early as 10ᵗʰ May 1783, to mark the memory of this great adventure. They created the Society of the Cincinnati and Louis XVI authorized the French officers of noble birth to become members. As well as de La Fayette and de Rochambeau, others included the Ducs de Broglie, de Levis-Mirepoix, and de Castries, and d'Aboville, de Tingey and the Comte de Saint-Simon[14]. The French branch, banned during the Revolution, was reconstituted in 1925 and a good number of the heads of the families of the descendants of the "liberators" still belong to it.

Descendants of the combatants have formed other associations, such as "The Sons and Daughters of the Revolution".

The Society of the Cincinnati on a visit to the shipyard (June 1999). AH.

---

[13] In memory of the *dictator* Lucius Quinctius Cincinnatus, who returned to being a simple ploughman after twice being Commander-in-Chief of the Roman infantry.
[14] Future founder of "Saint-Simonism" and nephew of the Duc de Saint-Simon, the famous memoirs writer.

Tree shapes usable in building ships.

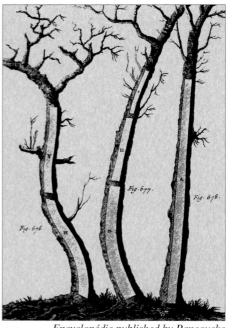

Engraving from ink drawing by Duhamel du Monceau,
photo MNM, Paris.

Encyclopédie published by Pancoucke
(1783-1792) photo MNM, Paris.

The tariff of Brest dated 16ᵗʰ November 1765, and the instruction dating from the year XI.

Counter-stem and transom beams

Wing-transom and upper deck knee

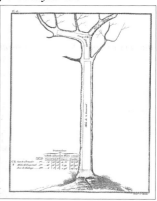

Rudder main pieces

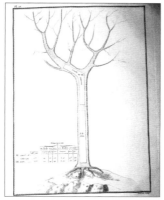

Head cheeks

Floor timber crotch

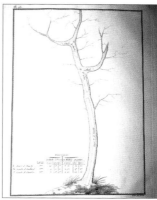

Deck beam and forecastle and quarterdeck knee

Chapter II
The Navy

Boats are born in the forest

)-gun frigate followed by a corvette. Drawing by Nicolas Ozanne, tutor a naval matters to Louis XVI and his brothers when children. Taken from e Recueil, a publication showing the different vessels used in war, for the struction of "the young future officers that the King is having trained in the orts" (document judged by Admiral Paris to date from 1760 to 1765).

In 1765, the States of Brittany launched the construction of the vessel, the Bretagne.

French kings and the fleet of the 17th and 18th centuries

Riled by English support to the rebellious Protestant port of La Rochelle, Richelieu urged the king to build a fleet capable of standing up to the English. On the deaths of Louis XIII and Richelieu (in 1643 and 1642), the French fleet had a strength of 20 galleys and 80 ships of the line. By the time of the death of Cardinal Mazarin in 1661, almost nothing remained of this fleet. As soon as he was old enough to assume political power, Louis XIV ordered the construction of a new fleet, despite the depleted state of the forests. In 1692, the king had at his disposal 110 ships of the line and 690 support vessels, manned by 70 000 sailors and carrying a total of 14 670 canons.

His successor, Louis XV, did not pursue this effort. After the heavy losses at the Battle of Quiberon Bay (1759) and the peace treaty of 1763, which cost France its colonies and paralysed its naval dockyards, the duc de Choiseul, the Minister of Foreign Affairs, War and the Navy, endeavoured, in spite of the Treasury being empty, to reconstitute a powerful fleet by subscription. Between 1762 and 1768, he asked towns and provinces to build ships of the line. This policy, which was continued by Sartine[1], endowed the French fleet with 274 ships by 1780. However, when Louis XVI wanted to face up to the English and to renovate the navy, he was often confronted with opposition from his ministers.

[1] Former Lieutenant General of the police, Navy Minister from 1774 to 1780.

LOUIS XVI, RENOVATOR OF THE FRENCH NAVY, PROTECTOR OF THE LIBERTY OF THE SEAS

Louis XVI, oil painting on canvas by Duplessis.

© *Musée des Beaux-Arts de Dijon.*

Immediately after acceding to the throne on May 10th 1774, Louis XVI cherished the ambition to guarantee the freedom of the seas for all nations, for he had suffered from seeing the French fleet blockaded in Brest and England assuming the right to inspect all merchant ships.

Exasperated by the attacks of English privateers, the king even granted the protection of his flag to any ship that requested it and the rebels in the American colonies profited from this. On May 2nd 1776, the king decided to help the "republic of the United States".

At the end of December 1777, the king hailed the independence of the United States. A pact was signed on February 6th 1778 "to uphold the liberty, the sovereignty and the absolute and unlimited independence of the United States in matters of government and of trade." By the end of the same month, a powerful naval squadron had been sent to the American coasts.

In 1780 Louis XVI opposed Vergennes, who wanted the most speedy peace, before provoking in 1781 the resignation of Necker, who found the reconstruction of the fleet too costly.

After the peace of 1783, he signed treaties confirming *"the liberty to navigate on the seas."*

THE FRENCH FLEET UNDER LOUIS XVI

A very great construction effort brought it close to the level of the English fleet :
1774 : 43 ships of the line and 34 frigates and corvettes (against 95 and 173 in England),
1782 : 72 and 65 frigates,
1786 : 81 and 130 frigates and corvettes,
1790 : 97 and 113 frigates and corvettes,.
The French navy had never been so powerful, but the Revolution caused it to sink back again.

The needs for shipbuilding wood and the world's forests

After Philippe VI de Valois in 1346, Colbert in the 17th century, with his edict of 1669, and Choiseul in the 18th century, demanded good management of French forests to satisfy the country's need for wood, a strategic raw material for shipbuilding and for masts. 3 000 oak trees were required for building one warship. Thanks to this foresight, France was conspicuously successful in providing wood for its shipbuilding and today still possesses flourishing forests. The counter-example is the former forests all round the shores of the Mediterranean, which were over-exploited and destroyed to build the navies of ancient powers. Today Greece is denuded of its forest, the Lebanon has devoured its cedars and the Aegean Islands, having lost their protective mantle of trees, are arid.

Chateaubriand rightly observed "the forests come before peoples and the deserts follow them." Colbert had understood, as did Choiseul after him, that without abundant forests it was impossible to have a powerful navy. The great reform of forests and water

The Bercé national forest, the fruit of the original decisions by Louis XIV and Colbert.

resources in 1669 structured and controlled the French forests, which were transformed into oak plantations. The resulting superb forests of mature trees can still be seen today. All the forests in the kingdom were called upon to make their contribution for the navy, so long as they were near to a waterway along which the wood could be transported. The remainder of the requirements were imported.

The works of Duhamel du Monceau, published in 1752, were authoritative in both naval matters and sylviculture, despite the regrettable influence of the physiocrats. The latter, with Voltaire, declared their opposition to the controlled management of forest plantation by the State and certain royal forests were even rashly put up for sale.

Frontispiece and title page of the work by Duhamel du Monceau, dated 1752, "Elements of Naval Architecture or Practical Treatise on the Construction of Vessels".

Ships of the line and frigates

Ships of the line from Sané's 74-gun design to the *Montebello*

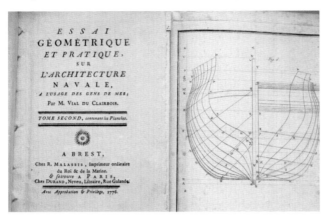

Geometrical and Practical Essay on Naval Architecture for the use of sea people by *Vial du Clairbois, 1776 : title page and fold-out draught.*

At the instigation of Duhamel du Monceau, the "masters of the axe", who passed on their skills and worked without drawings, were gradually replaced by engineers and standardized designs. Ships of the same rank in a squadron should be able to sail at the same speed. For the first time, vessels of a common model were built, such as the 74-gun type designed by the leading architect *Sané* in 1781.

The *Montebello* was one of the largest wooden warships ever built. Launched in 1813, during Napoleon's Empire, this 120-gun First-rate 3 decker had a displacement of 5 000 tons. Her deck was 75 metres long and 12 metres wide, her sides towered 9.65 metres above the water and the top of her main-mast was 71 metres above her keel. Fully manned for war, she had a crew of 1085. Her 12 400 m² of sail could be furled in less than two minutes by 334 hands.

The Montebello, *launched 1813, monster of the seas, one of the largest wooden three-deckers. When the Royal Forestry School was founded at Nancy in 1824, a 1/40th scale model was made for the instruction of future officers of the Water and Forests service on ship construction and the search for suitable timber* Photo musée national de la Marine.

What is a frigate ?

Frigates were smaller and less heavily armed warships than the ships of the line having two or three covered gun decks. As their tasks were scouting for squadrons, carrying orders and escort duties, they needed to be particularly swift.

In the 17th century, frigates' armament was very light, varying from 26 12pdr guns to 28 18pdrs. Jean Bart initiated the move to use frigates instead of cumbersome ships of the line to harry English merchant vessels. As frigates were less expensive to build and were light and speedy, considerable numbers of them were commissioned. The decree issued by Louis XV in 1765 defined them as being 36 to 39 metres long, carrying 20 to 40 guns and being crewed by 130 to 300 men.

The Hermione *is a typical example of an 18th century 12pdr frigate[2].*

In the course of time, 12pdr frigates became gradually larger and more powerful and in Louis XVI's reign they had thirty or more guns[3]. They continued to gain weight until the middle of the 19th century; when their scouting role was taken over by a smaller class of ship, the corvette.

FROM SIZES OF SHIP TO OFFICER'S RANKS

Single masted boats : cutters, like Surcouf's *Renard*, were adopted by privateers because of their speed and manoeuvrability. By the War of American Independence, their hull length had reached 26 metres and they carried around 20 guns.

Two masted : schooners (30 to 90 tons and six, eight or even ten guns) and brigs (500 to 1 000 tons, carrying 18 to 22 18pdr or 24pdr carronades).

Three masted : corvette, frigate and ship of the line with 2 or 3 gun decks.

The hierarchy of French naval officer's ranks was determined by the ships on which they served (equivalent rank in land army in brackets): midshipman, 2nd class ensign (2nd lieutenant) 1st class ensign (lieutenant) 1st lieutenant (captain) lieutenant commander[4] (commander) commander (lieutenant-colonel) captain (colonel) rear-admiral (**) vice-admiral (***) squadron vice-admiral (****) and admiral (*****).

The schooner Recouvrance *from Brest*

Amiral, strange title coming to us from the seas of the Levant, deriving from the Arabic *amir al bahr,* meaning "Prince or Emir of the Sea".

The Duguay-Trouin, *a Sané designed 74-gun 2-decker, built at Rochefort in 1796, veteran of Trafalgar, kept afloat by the British, could and should have been preserved like her contemporary, Nelson's* Victory. *The British offered to give back to France this 150 year old ship in a bad state of repair. When the French refused to take her, she was sunk in the Channel on November 2nd 1949, flying both nations' flags and with the honours of both navies.*

Photo musée national de la Marine, Rochefort.

---

[2] From the Greek *aphracte*, transformed into *fregata* in Italian.
[3] The *Hermione* carried 32 12pdrs.
[4] Rank created in 1831

The Hermione *under construction. Half of the frame ribs have been put in place. The 1/18th scale model of the* Hermione, *visible lower left, is assembled by Jean Thomas, as the main project progresses, in order to guide the shipwrights.* Photo AH.

Chapter III
From yesterday to today, the design of the *Hermione*

Her construction in 1779

The *Hermione*, a swift ship with a generous sail plan, like all frigates, was one of a class of six ships in the naval renovation programme of Louis XVI. The decision to build her was taken on October 23rd 1778, work started in the boatyard in December, the last inspection before launching took place on April 19th 1779 and rigging was completed on April 30th 1779. Construction had been rushed through in less than six months, which was exceptionally quick, but it had required "33 000 of the King's days".

The *Hermione* is a 12pdr frigate[1] carrying 32 guns firing canon balls weighing 12 pounds (5.5 kg), with a speed of 10 knots close-hauled and nearly 13 knots large (broad reach, wind athwart). She is 44.27 m long, 11.20 m in the beam and 5.78 m high from the keel to the midship deck beam. Her angle of heel could reach 20° to 45° according to whether the gun-ports were open or closed.[2] Having

The Dédaigneuse, *a 12pdr frigate launched in Bordeaux in 1776, probably quite similar to the* Hermione, *is an additional historic source guiding her reconstruction. In both ships, only the foremost gun-port, the bridle port for the chaser gun, facing waves and spray, was fitted with a deadlight.*

Musée national de la Marine de Rochefort.

reached the sea on May 21st 1779, she engaged in her first action on her first outing on May 29th and 30th ! She returned to Rochefort and in November 1779 was put into the double graving dock to have her bottom sheathed in copper, which considerably improved her speed.

THE HERMIONE'S SISTERS

Two sister ships, the *Concorde* and the *Courageuse*, were launched in 1777 and a third, the *Fée* accompanied the Hermione in 1779. The Concorde was captured by the English on February 15th 1783 and was incorporated into the Royal Navy, at which time the sheer and profile draughts were taken off. These have provided the drawings being used today. Two very similar half-sisters, the *Charmante* and the *Junon* were also launched in 1777.

---

[1] She also had six to eight 6pdr guns and other weapons.
[2] Information provided by the CRAIN, Centre de Recherche pour l'Architecture et l'Industrie Nautique : Philippe Pallu de la Barrière.

The wreck on the Four bank

Success at last for Michel Vazquez in recuperating a first canon from the wreck during the campaign in 2005. Photo AFP, Franck Perry.

On September 20th 1793, the *Hermione*, with a reduced crew, left the Loire estuary to escort to Brest a convoy loaded with canons coming from the Indret foundry. The incompetence of the replacement pilot, "who mistook one landmark for another[3]" caused her to be wrecked on the Four bank off Le Croisic, following a navigational error. He was judged to be wholly responsible and was put in prison.

The wreck was located on July 22nd 1984 by the marine archaeologist Michel Vazquez and his team. It was an extraordinary stroke of luck to find the *Hermione* just when a project was afoot to build a replica. What remained of her ?

- Canons, of which one 6pdr dated 1783 was a replacement for a gun damaged after the American campaign.
- One of the anchors, 4.25 metres high and weighing 1.5 tons.
- Grapeshot boxes : tin boxes with wooden lids filled with lead shot, which was simply tipped into the gun muzzle.
- A brace and a pintle, parts of a bronze hinge between rudder and stern-post.
- Parts of the wooden framing giving the scantling (thickness and breadth) of the ribs and their distance apart, the frame disposition, varying from 95 to 105 mm.
- Ballast of iron pigs and shingle.

The name Hermione

Mythology holds that she was the daughter of Menelaus, King of Sparta and founder of Lacedaemon, and of the very beautiful Helen, leading figure of the Iliad and cause of the Trojan War. As Helen was the daughter of Okeanos, in other words of the Ocean, Hermione was the grand-daughter of the Ocean ! In *Andromaque,* Racine depicts her as lovelorn and jealous.

Nine French frigates have borne this name, the first one in 1669. La Fayette's was the fifth. They were followed by two submarines. The second frigate, built in 1748 at Rochefort, was the first to be armed with 12pdr guns. She was captured by the English in 1757 and was renamed *HMS Unicorn Prize.* The British Royal Navy has also had 7 ships named Hermione.

---

[3] Quoted in L'*Hermione* by Kalbach and Gireaud, published by Dervy.

In memory of La Fayette : frigates of yesterday and today

Can one compare our ship with the furtive frigate *La Fayette*[4], the cost of which would allow the construction of fifty *Hermiones*? Obviously not. Let us however imagine the improbable encounter of the third type. What would happen if the furtive frigate suddenly found herself confronted by fifty 18th century frigates returning from the Bermuda triangle? In the end, reconstructing the *Hermione* is perhaps whimsical but not unreasonable !

The improbable encounter : the frigate Hermione *1779-1793 and the furtive frigate* La Fayette *1996.*
Watercolour by André Lambert

The *Hermione* of yesterday and today		The frigate *La Fayette*
Date	1779, then 1997 to 2011	1993
Dimensions	44 m by 11 m	125 to 135 m by 15 m
Displacement	1 200 king's tuns	2 500 then 3 600 tons
Type of power	Sail and now also auxiliary engine	4 engines – 21 000 hp
Speed	13 knots maximum	25 knots
Crew	313 hands originally, 30 professional sailors today	12 officers and 129 NCOs and crew
Class	4 12pdr frigates	5 France, 6 Taiwan, 3 Saudi Arabia
Cost	Today 17 million euros	1 billion euros
Duration of construction	6 months, today 15 years	In 1979 30 months, today 6 months

---

[4] Since 1993, the new French "light frigates" are called "La Fayette type frigates" FLF.

Comparison between several replicas

In numerous countries with a strong maritime tradition, replicas of lost ships have been constructed and there has been a movement to preserve and restore the maritime heritage

SHIP	RENARD	RECOUVRANCE	PRIDE OF BALTIMORE	ETOILE & BELLE-POULE	H.M.S. ROSE	GOTHEBORG	HERMIONE	BATAVIA
Country	France	France	USA	France	USA	Sweden	France	Netherlands
Masts	1	2	2	2	3	3	3	3
Height above water	26	28	30	30	40	47	54	
Draught	2.8	3.2	3.8	3.5	3.9	5.18	5.7	
Hull length	19	25	29.4	25.3	41	40.9	44.2	56.6 ??
Overall length	30	42	51	32.35	54	58.5	65	56.6
Breadth	6	6.4	7.9	7.2	9.7	10.4	11.24	10.6
Displacement Displacement	70 44.5	80 148	185	180	500	1 232 1 550	1200	
Crew in war	60	50 à 60	-	-	-	-	313	-
Crew today	4	5				30	60	
Passengers	12 to 30	25				50 (80)	-	
Guns	10 8pdrs 4 4pdrs	12	-	-	-	14	26 12pdrs 8 6pdrs	-
Sail area	249	440		425		1941	1200	1190
N° sails	4	12	12	12	26	26	26	
Construction Reconstruction	1812 1990	1817 1991 to 1993	1835 1977 and 1988	1931 1932	1757 1970	1740 1993 to 2003	1779 1997 to 2013	1628 1982 to 1995

Other sea-worthy replicas

The *Renard* of Saint-Malo, authorized to carry members of the public, has 8pdr carronades cast in aluminium instead of iron, each weighing 150 kg rather than the original 450 kg.

The *Batavia* : keel laid in 1985, built with great concern for historical exactness. Cannot sail at night. Taken to Australia – aboard a cargo ship. Undertakes limited day sailing.

The *Grand Turk*, (GB) 22-gun sixth-rate frigate seen in the TV series "Hornblower" is a replica of H.M.S. Blandford, built in the mid-18th century.

The Recouvrance of Brest, a good quality replica, has 8 gun-ports, of which 2 on each side are fakes, and she will one day have her 12 guns. In the background can be seen one of the two schooners of the French navy, Etoile or Belle-Poule.

The Gotheborg : *this ship plying the silk route was wrecked on September 12th 1745. The construction of the replica has taken 10 years and incorporates modern adaptations including 7 watertight bulkheads. Her masts and all her rigging are historically correct. Since June 6th 2003, she has sailed as a passenger vessel.* Photo AH

The H.M.S. Rose *(USA) at Brest in 1996. A replica of a* British frigate *which took part in the American War of Independence. Although distinctly smaller than the* Hermione, *this is the ship which is most closely similar, by her construction and date. She has featured in several films.*

The Pride of Baltimore *(USA) in the Brest roadstead in 1996. A comparable schooner to the Recouvrance.*

3-3. The draughts of the *Hermione*

The draughts of the *Hermione* have not been found, but the British had taken off draughts[5] of her sister-ship the Concorde, after capturing her in 1783. With other documents, these have served as the basic reference. Mr Bernard Moreau and the CRAIN, Centre de Recherches pour l'Architecture et l'Industrie Nautique, directed by Mr Philippe Pallu de la Barrière, have carried out a major job in reconstituting the various draughts of the ship.

Since June 2003, another naval architect has been responsible for managing the construction project. Paradoxically, the *Asselin* company, specialists in restoring the wooden structures of buildings, particularly historical monuments, were selected after a public tender procedure for the job of building the *Hermione*, naturally with shipwrights.

ASSELIN S.A., Frégate'HERM
Relevé du tracé
J.T 07/2002

Wing-transom
Square fashion-piece
Oblique fashion-piece

Lisse de hourdy

Estain carré

Estain oblique

Vertical des formes

Body plan of the Hermione *with the waterlines and the forward ribs (right half) and stern ribs (left half).* Jean Thomas, Asselin SA.

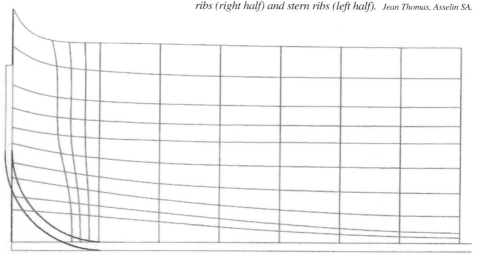

---

[5] Now in the National Maritime Museum, Greenwich.

28

1/18ᵗʰ scale model of the Hermione *by Jean Thomas, cabinetmaker, draughtsman and naval historian, made as the reconstruction progressed in order to guide the shipwrights.*

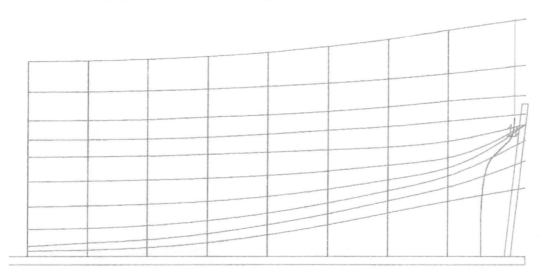

Profile draught of the Hermione, *showing the bow ribs to the left.* Jean Thomas, Asselin SA.

JEAN THOMAS

Both shipwright and historian, Jean Thomas is a professional cabinetmaker who has become a draughtsman and model maker. He has synchronized the making of a 1/18th scale "shipyard model" of the *Hermione* with the progress of the ship itself. Begun in September 1996, this model enables the shipwrights to see precisely the piece that they are about to shape from the full-sized timber and the visitors to follow the stages of the advancing project.

Jean Thomas taking infinite pains with his model. Photo AH, Francis Latreille.

It is often with reluctance that Jean Thomas is obliged to make concessions required by safety regulations. As he says with amusement "getting the Hermione to take to sea today is like wanting to make a de Dion Bouton car pass a technical safety test (MOT) !"

In the 18th century, at a period when draughts were not used, the king ordered that models should be made of the best performing ships, so that their qualities could be reproduced in other vessels. For teaching purposes, larger scale models were also produced with the greatest meticulousness for the naval dockyards, each component being an exact reduced scale replica of the original.

One can understand the difference between a decorative model in which only the visible exterior is accurate and this working model with planking fitted on the starboard side and the framing exposed on the port side.

Jean Thomas gazes at his model of which he can justly be proud. Never without his pipe, like Jean Bart, who when criticised by a courtier, replied "I have the right to smoke my pipe on the King's ships during battle, so I have the right to do so in his antechambers (at Versailles)."

Historical accuracy and modern constraints

Concessions to lighten the work in the shipyard

It is fortunate that the skills of the shipwrights can nowadays be assisted with modern techniques and equipment, for the important point is that the raw material should be respected, that the wood grain direction should be preserved and that the shipwright can do fine work, as in the past.

It is also necessary that the work and heavy moving should be carried out in safety, without difficult conditions and dangerous loads and that work regulations should be adhered to.

The work in former times. Lifting of ships' timbers with a "squirrel cage" crane in the port of Brest around 1850. The masting sheers can be seen in the background. Detail of an oil painting by Pierre Julien Gilbert (1783-1860). Musée national de la Marine à Paris, photo P. Dantec.

Wholly modern techniques. For the heavy curved ribs of the Hermione, *to be cut from a thick slab of oak, a chain saw with tilting head guide. Photo AH.*

The use of traditional techniques. The adze, sometimes indispensable, is still used. Photo AH.

The aims of the association

The association wanted to build an exact replica of the Hermione, rediscover the skills of the shipwrights of the period and appreciate all the difficulties and the hardships of such an undertaking. Then to install masts, rigging and sails and, in memory of La Fayette, at least retrace his route to the United States before returning to Rochefort during the summer months in order to welcome admirers !

But today's maritime authorities will never allow sailors to voyage as their predecessors did in the 18th century. It is considered too dangerous and the principle of precaution and the respect for modern norms are incompatible with the spirit of adventure. Nonetheless, the ship will be historically authentic with no watertight bulkheads and with her orlop deck too low for a man to stand upright.

The association's logo. Photo AH.

For an Atlantic crossing to be authorized, the entire construction must meet current norms, checked by an external certification organization, the Veritas agency. Modern navigational instruments, such as GPS, are required, which poses no problem. Another requirement was that the *Hermione* should be fitted with two inboard engines driving two propellers, to cope with emergencies, such as a man overboard, and to be more autonomous and manoeuvrable when entering and leaving harbour. Electricity is needed on board, and therefore generators, in particular for the fire detectors and for the electric windlasses for weighing anchor instead of calling on 60 sailors to man the large capstan with levers.

To simplify matters, the *Hermione* will be classed, not as a passenger vessel but as a leisure craft.

The reconstitution of a really authentic replica necessitates considerable research work and the participation of recognized naval historians, like Jean Boudriot, seen here visiting the Hermione shipyard in the company of Jean Thomas, expert and model maker. Photo AH.

Compromises and concessions

Arduous discussions have been held on the subject of historical accuracy and present day restrictions. The pins and other sorts of broach will be made of bronze and sometimes of stainless steel when they are not visible. Does it really matter if the hidden pins, which go through 1 to 3 metres of oak to hold together the stern-post body and the keel assembly, are in corrosion prone iron or in stainless steel? This little liberty will give a welcome extension to the ship's lifespan. The *Hermione* will be just like her forebear, but will be longer lasting. For it is also one of the aims that the *Hermione*, afloat in her dock, should be able to be admired by visitors for a very long time, with minimal maintenance costs.

In the same way, the gun carriages and trucks were always made of elm to reduce the wood splinters which could cause appalling carnage among the gun crews. But elm wood is no longer available, because of the ravages of "Dutch elm disease" and so they have inevitably had to be made from other kinds of wood. Nobody is obliged to achieve the impossible!

RAYMOND LABBÉ

The former owner of a shipyard, son and grandson of shipwrights, during his long career Raymond Labbé had built almost two hundred boats, including large wooden trawlers and several sizeable replicas, such as the bisquine[6] *La Cancalaise* and Surcouf's cutter *Renard*. A great specialist of wood framing, he travelled frequently from St Malo to Rochefort to preside over shipyard meetings. His experience was indispensable for launching the project and laying down procedures for a job which was to go on for at least ten years. For the national heritage evening in September 1993, it was he who set up in the double dry dock a metal skeleton of the *Hermione's* hull enabling people to visualize its size.

What had only been a dream had been transformed into a real project. He expressed himself forcefully and knew how to adapt to modernity, saying "It is not because they made stupid mistakes in the 18th century that we are obliged to reproduce them."

After his death in 2005, his role was taken on by Gérard Bernard, a trawler builder at Saint-Vaast la Hougue and restorer of *Marité* and *Fleur de Lampaul*.

Raymond Labbé, on the left, with Philippe Pallu de la Barrière, the founding architect of the project, and Benedict Donnelly, the president of the association, on the right (February 1997). Photo AH.

Full scale hull skeleton in the double graving dock. Photo AH.

[6] bisquine, a traditional type of fishing boat, originally from the Bay of Bisquay, mainly used off the Norman and Breton coasts around the Mont St Michel.

The Véritas Agency and safety measures

Large wooden ships have not been built for a century and in the meantime the principle of precaution has taken priority. Lacking appropriate norms, the very prudent control agency first of all applied the regulations of 1963 for the last 30 metre long trawlers before chancing on those of 1928 covering the larger Icelandic schooners. But simply scaling everything up may produce excesses. The hooked splice joints and scarphed end joints have been lengthened beyond the practices of the 18th century and the thickness of the keelson has been doubled. As the work progresses the precautions increase and the specifications of Duhamel du Monceau or of Sané are largely exceeded !

As for the deck beams, they are single pieces of curved wood, whereas they were originally often made up of two half-beams jointed in the centre with hooked splice joints.

Screw propulsion will be provided. A real chain and a modern anchor are obligatory for navigation and electric windlasses will help to raise them.

Duhamel du Monceau, Paris 1700 – 1782 : firstly botanist in the royal garden at Versailles, subsequently General Inspector of the Navy.

SHIPS' STABILITY

Ballast, consisting of stones, shingle, spare canons and stocks of canon balls, is lodged in the bottom of the hold. As the stability is improved if the centre of gravity is low, the upper parts of the ship's hull and the masts and rigging are made as light as is possible. In a three-decker, the lowest gun-deck carries the largest calibre guns, which are the heaviest, the middle gun-deck has medium calibre guns and the upper battery has the lightest pieces. Ships of the line which had been cut down by the removal of their upper gun-deck and superstructures were referred to as rasées. The object was to cure problems of poor stability and to make these ships safer and more rapid. An overloaded, top-heavy vessel could be given better sailing qualities by this means.

THE SINKING OF THE VASA IN THE 17TH CENTURY

The King of Sweden determined to build the largest ship possible to demonstrate his superiority. This superb monument[7] in oak rose high above the water and its 'aft castle' towered 19 metres above the sea. Overladen with nearly 500 pieces of sculpture and 64 guns, she heeled over at the first gust of wind on her inaugural outing, despite the ballast of 120 tons of stones. Water poured into the open ports of the lower gun-deck and she sank in front of Stockholm with many families aboard. She had already shown herself to be so unstable that the stability tests had been interrupted, but nobody had dared tell the king, who had so much wanted this vessel and approved the plans !

[7] Brought up from the sea-bed and preserved in a museum in Stockholm, the 69 m long Vasa is definitely worth a visit.

The sort of crooked tree that was so useful for the navy.

Chapter IV

Supplying the construction project

The wood for the *Hermione* of 1779

Heavily knotted oak, giving wood with cat's paw markings, not suitable for furniture but perfect for shipbuilding.

Good quality wood

Oak of "shipbuilding" quality is a vigorous, hard, quick growing wood, not suitable for use by cabinetmakers. Naval dockyards refuse wood with frost splits, detached growth rings, double sapwood or twisted fibres. Coniferous softwood of mast and spar quality, having to be supple, with fine growth rings, is very different from quick growing trees from the plains.

All the forests in the kingdom that were near to a waterway were explored by the navy, as the supply of shipbuilding wood from the forestry basins depended on the inland waterway network. The navy left a deep mark on the forests. The Grandes Ventes district of the Tronçais forest bears witness to a great felling ; the Marine section of the Cranou forest near Brest and the Royale forester's lodge section of the Chaux forest show traces of having supplied oaks for ships' hulls. As for the Marine forest track and forester's lodge in the Joux forest, they are a reminder of the descent of the tall fir trees to be used as masts.

With shipbuilding timber, for every use a specific wood

Naval construction consumed huge quantities of wood[1] until iron and steel began to be used around 1850. The main species used were :

---

[1]For more complete details on the protection of the forests for the navy, refer to the book *Bois de marine* ou *250 réponses aux questions des amoureux de la forêt*, by the same author and the same publisher. (No English version)

- for the submerged parts of the structure or shell of the ship, oak and elm,
- for the planking of the hull below the water line, oak for warships, cyprus, cedar and beech for merchant vessels,
- for the planks of the bulwarks and of the top deck, the "roof" of the ship, fir and pine,
- for the gun-decks, strong oak in the areas under the guns, including the recoil zone,
- for the oars, beech or ash,
- for the caps of the masts, bilge water pumps and pulley blocks, elm,
- for the masts and spars, light and supple conifers, having grown slowly and with fine growth rings,
- for the sheaves of the pulleys, holm oak, box, or guaiacum.

One of those very curved pieces which require wood with matching fibre pattern. François Asselin.

The wood grain and the revenge of curved woods

Trees grow by the yearly addition of a peripheral layer, the fibres and sap ducts being parallel to the axis of the trunk or of the branch. By respecting the alignment of the fibres, particularly by splitting the wood lengthways, one can obtain thin slats of high strength and springiness like skis. On the other hand, if the wood is sawed across the grain, it has little strength. But in a ship everything is curved and, in order to be robust, needs to have all its components cut from naturally curved pieces of wood. Such pieces result from the search for light, part of the struggle for survival between trees.

Sometimes the most misshapen and crooked trees provide the most perfect curved futtocks[2] or the best knees. Spurned and rejected because of their deformity, they get their revenge and earn the gratitude of the shipwright.

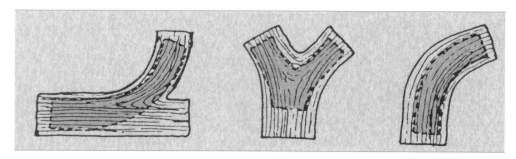

The necessity of following the direction of the grain means that pieces for ships must be cut from trees having naturally the same shape.

The search for crooked wood[3]

These crooked trees, born two or three centuries ago, were sought in all the forests in France or in international trade, subject to strict controls in wartime. It was better for the kingdom to have its own forests in good condition. The lack of curved wood was such that attempts were even made to increase its occurrence by increasing the forest edge lines, through the creation of clearings and tracks. Sometimes trees were constrained with the aim of inducing them to produce the desired curvatures or bends.

Ships' ribs are cut from curved trees that are difficult to find, above all in large sizes such as those needed for the Hermione. As François Asselin's shipwrights liked to joke "big bent specimens are more numerous in mankind than in trees !"

The standardized classification of wood at the time of the *Hermione's* birth

The "tariff" of Brest, issued on November 16th 1765, the beginning of the standardization of pieces for shipbuilding, and then that of March 15th 1783, were quite rightly incorporated into the Navy Instructions, produced in the year XI (1803). It consisted of a catalogue describing the pieces needed, according to their shape and their curvature, enabling the shipwright to order them without leaving his dockyard. Searches were undertaken for him, far away in the forests.

The pieces were classed into three categories :
- "Straight" pieces, destined for keels, stern-posts, rudder main pieces and bitts, as well as boards sawn up into thick planks for the external or internal planking of the hull,
- "Curved" pieces having a slight single curve, S shape or, a very rare phenomenon, curved in two different planes. The latter were used for the wing-transom or stern-most poop timber,
- "Knee" pieces, having a right-angle formed by the junction between the trunk and a large branch.

Straight wood.   *Curved wood.*   *Wood for knees.*

---

[2] "Genou" in French, which does not correspond to the English term "knee", refers to the most sharply bent section of a rib. This term was used from the end of the 18th century onwards. The French translation of "knee" is "courbe".
[3] See the book *Bois de marine* by the same author and the same publisher.

Signs and types

In order to transport only useful wood, the trunks were squared off and trimmed on the spot in the forest, in accordance with the Brest tariff and its nomenclature "sign and type".

The signs defined the shape and the utilization of the piece : keel, stem, bitt, deck beam, knee, futtock, floor-timber, rider, etc. The shape of these pieces varied according to their position along the ship between the stem and the stern, the V of the floor-timber, for example, being more or less open or acute.

The *seven types* specified the dimensions of the "sign", which depended on the size of the ship, whether launch, cutter, advice-boat, brig, corvette, frigate or ship of the line.

TARIF

ARRÊTÉ à Brest le 16 novembre 1765,

Des Proportions que doivent avoir les Pièces de Bois de construction , pour faire la différence des espèces dans lesquelles elles doivent entrer; ensemble de l'Arc que doivent avoir celles qui en sont susceptibles ;

SAVOIR :

1.ʳᵉ ESPÈCE.	PIEDS de longueur.	POUCES de largeur.	POUCES d'épaisseur au milieu.	ARC par pied de longueur de dehors en dehors.	OUVERTURE des courbes de dehors en dehors.
A Quille...........	.36à50.	.16à20.	.16à20.		
AB Brion ou ringeot...	.18.30.	.16.20.	.16.20.	....	de 110 à 160 deg.
B Étrave...........	.24.36.	.20.36.	.16.20.	de 9 à 16 lignes..	
D Contre-étrave......	.18.22.	.20.24.	.16.20.	de 12 à 8 lignes...	
C Étambot...........	.28.36.	.20.30.	.16.20.		

The indispensable curved pieces for shipbuilding, from wood to iron

The main categories among the angled knees necessary for building ships were :
- the very large stern-post knees, joining the keel and the stern-post,
- the fore foot knees, between the keel and the stem,
- the hanging knee between the stem and the cut-water,
- the cheeks of the head[4], lodging knees joining the bows and the cut-water,
- the deck knees, hanging knees joining the deck beams to the ship's sides,
- the small knees, serving as pedestals for small boarding canons on the top.

All these knees, both hanging (vertical) and lodging (horizontal), are used as joining pieces and reinforcements, bracing the frame and preventing distortion of the ship. These timbers, rare and so hard to find for large ships, were often the main factor limiting naval construction. No angled pieces, no ships !

---

[4] Not to be confused with the cheeks at the top of the lower mast, supporting the top platform.

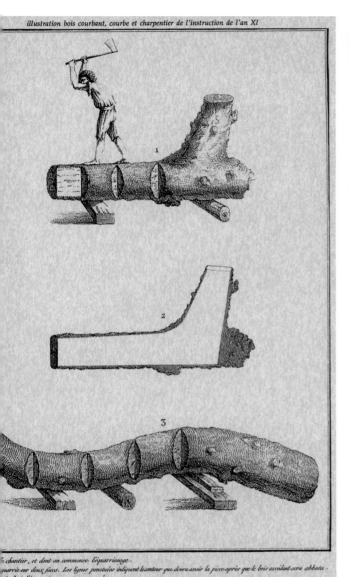

illustration bois courbant, courbe et charpentier de l'instruction de l'an XI

; chantier, et dont en commence l'équarrissage.
quarrie sur deux faces. Les lignes ponctuées indiquent le contour que devra avoir la pièce après que le bois excédant sera abbatu .
nt dent l'équarrissage est commencé.

National forest of Cranou, near to Brest : looking to cut out a fine knee with the author. DR.

Shipwright in the forest cutting out a large knee : drawing attached to the Tarif de Brest, *dating from 1765 and 15th March 1783, re-used for the shipbuilding instruction issued by the Forestry Administration in the year XI, (i.e. 1803).*

The instructions of the Navy were very precise concerning the search for knees ready for cutting and the preservation of "potential knees", those for the Navy of the future ! Despite this, there were never enough of them.

So, during a period of particular shortage, in the mid-18th century, the French dockyards invented assembled knees, with two jointed pieces reinforced by an iron bracket, as on the *Hermione*, and then wholly iron knees. When the ship of the line *Invincible*[5] was captured by the English, they were astounded to find the use of iron knees on this vessel which was larger and swifter than their admiral's ship.

---

[5] Built in 1741 and captured in 1747. See *La Grande Époque de la Marine à Voile*, by Martine Acerra and Jean Meyer.

Wooden knees

1. *Installing a hanging knee on the* Hermione.

2. *A handsome row of knees beneath the orlop deck*

3. *Deck beam knees on the* Hermione, *in the large cabin at the end of the gun deck.*

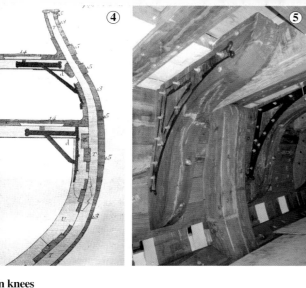

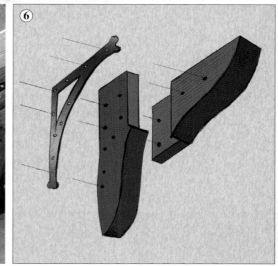

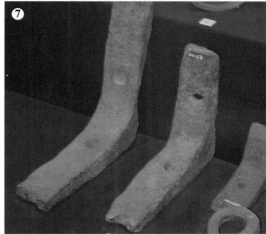

n knees

Already in the mid-18th century, there was a shortage of wooden knees iron bracing was tried out. *Drawing by Duhamel du Monceau (1752).*

Corresponding jointed deck beam knee on the Hermione.

In the absence of a single piece of naturally curved wood, knees were de up from jointed timber and reinforced with a metal bracket.

ron knees found at Vanikoro, the site of the wrecks of the two frigates, Boussole and L'Astrolabe, *composing the expedition commanded by* Pérouse, 1785. *Musée de la Marine à Paris.*

Knees made of formed sheet metal plates on the reconstruction of IS Rose. *Note the table-bunks on the gun deck.*

Hammering and hammers

The abandon of hammering[6]

For the past six centuries, foresters have used forester's hammers to mark their choice of trees to be felled and of those to be preserved for the future. They have in this manner shaped the forests. The hammer is a kind of small axe with a raised stamp on the butt end. The cutting edge is used to remove a flake of bark to expose a smooth surface of bare wood. The woodman then strikes with the hammer face to mark the wood, as though he were a moneyer striking coin.

A hammerer in Gâvre forest

Forester's hammers.

From 1992 onwards, foresters have resumed the practice of hammering for shipbuilding, hence the inscribed anchor, seen here in Rennes Forest.

What hammers ?

Trees for shipbuilding were marked with an anchor. Any misappropriation for civilian uses of a trunk marked with the anchor was severely punished. There were hammers to designate trees in the forest and hammers for use by dockyard staff handling reception. Trees that were refused were marked with a rejection hammer and documents were issued authorizing their return to commercial circuits.

The hammers used in the reign of Louis XVI for the *Hermione* bore the anchor beneath a fleur de lys[7].

Stamp of the hammer designating trees for the navy, model 1763, the period preceding the Hermione's *construction.*

---

[6] In former times, there also existed the inverse system whereby the trees to be preserved were marked, all the others being for felling.

[7] For further information on hammers and hammering, see *Bois de marine* by the same author.

Felling and transport

Felling[8]

Felling of suitable oaks is carried out by "extraction of the stump" in order to recuperate the entire tree, which sometimes has a bend at the base of the bole. Very early on, felling in winter was made obligatory, always outside the period when the sap is rising, except for broad-leaved trees, and preferably with a waning moon for the greatest durability of the wood.

Delimbing and topping : a woodsman climbs up to the very top of the tree and cuts off all the branches in order to avoid the danger of the trunk splitting when it falls. La Louve oak tree in the Gâvre forest in the Loire-Atlantique, with the inscription "La Fayette, nous voila.".
Photo : Jean-Philippe Combe, ONF.

Cutting up

Wood buyers have an unfortunate tendency to "straighten up" crooked oaks when bucking them (cutting into sections) in order to make them easier to transport. The cutting process must retain the desired curves and maximize their specific usefulness. On the left, conventional bucking for sawmill purposes and on the right, cutting up for shipbuilding.

Squaring off

As it was impossible to transport heavy lumber over great distances, it rapidly became clear that it was better to square off or trim the framing timber and ships' knees in the forest, enabling only the useful wood to be transported, leaving it only slightly over-dimensioned. The pieces would then be reduced in the shipyard to their precise dimensions. Later on, at the beginning of the 19th century, the ribs would be sawed mechanically in the dockyards with a double saw having two parallel blades. This permitted the recuperation of useful offcuts, which otherwise would have been lost as shavings. Refer to the preceding section *Tarif de Brest*, dated 16th November 1765, "sign and type", (pages 40 and 41).

Extrication and log skidding

When the tree had been felled, it had to be moved away from the stump area and got into a clearing before being dragged along under a skidder. Hauling in the forest was done using oxen and then horses took over on paved roads outside the forest. The lumber lifted by the skidder was dragged to the nearest river pick up point, where it was loaded on to a lighter, which took it away from the shore before transferring it onto river transport boats called flutes (after the Dutch 'fluyt').

Transport on flutes

In the 18th century, flutes were quite large military transport boats, sometimes old frigates with their guns removed. They were used for carrying shipbuilding timber and all the other types of materials, equipment and stores needed to build, equip and arm naval vessels.

The best oak was reserved for larger fighting ships and more ordinary wood, or even rejected timber, was used for slow sailing freight craft, giving rise to the sneering and pejorative expression "wood from which flutes are made".

The wood for the *Hermione* of today, from the forests of Poitou to…Versailles

The forests of Poitou, Brittany, Pays de la Loire, the surroundings of Paris and even Versailles have supplied the oak for the *Hermione*. What a magnificent symbol that oak trees of the park of the Chateau de Versailles and of the Trianon, having been mown down by the gales in 1999, should offer their wood to the new *Hermione*. They had witnessed Louis XVI decide to help the nascent American nation. The similarity between the Hermione of 1779 and her replica perhaps extends to the origin in Versailles of some timbers from trees either standing or blown down by the storms of 1774 and 1999 !

Recuperation operations at Versailles in the winter of 1774 – 1775 after a gale. Officers in uniform have come to pay a visit, particularly with a view to inspecting the fallen elms. Only 219 specimens, a fifth of the total number, were judged to be fit for building ships. Were some of them sent to Rochefort ? In the left middle distance, a tree is being felled by being uprooted, in order to get the whole trunk. Two men are digging and cutting the roots while a climber has just attached a rope on which 4 men are already pulling. In the foreground, two woodcutters are splitting up a trunk with wedges and mallet while three lengthwise sawyers are working on the spot so that only useful wood will have to be transported. Painting dated 1776 by Hubert Robert, The Baths of Apollo, Museum of the Chateau de Versailles and the Trianon. Photo Réunion des musées nationaux.

La Louve (she-wolf) oak tree, 380 years old, in plot 75 of the Gâvre national forest, condemned for being dangerous and because of its great age, has been sent to be used in the Hermione. The last wolf in the Loire Atlantique region was killed here.

The search for crooked wood for the Hermione of today

If supplies of straight oak do not pose any problem, the search for crooked trees is quite another matter, to be tackled by the Asselin company and by the association itself. More than 5 000 trees with a total volume of 10 000 m³ have been used, but only 1 200 m³ have been fashioned and installed on the frigate. The remainder has been put to other uses or sold for firewood by the association.

There used to be a service responsible for the supervision of timber for ship building, but it was "indefinitely suspended" in 1839 "considering that the Navy was able to obtain supplies of oak without the help of the hammering system regulating the forests and that the beneficiaries of supply contracts could be entrusted with the task of searching for suitable trees themselves." This service having been disbanded and the network of specialists having disappeared, the shipwrights, carrying templates for the pieces they want, are sometimes obliged to visit felling operations in the forests to look for suitable crooked trees.

If the shipyard finds a batch of curved wood, the shipwrights go to the wood storage zone at Rochefort, here also with the help of their templates, to find appropriate timber from which they can shape the piece required.

Felling in the national forest of Gâvre in the Loire-Atlantique, by uprooting the tree so as to recuperate all of the wood for the Hermione, *with no waste. Photo AH.*

Offcuts being sold as firewood to happy customers, in the shipyard in November 1999. Photo AH.

RAW MATERIAL REQUIRED

Oak : 1 200 m³	Ironwork : 35 tons	Oakum 3 tons
Softwood : 205 m³	Pitch : 1 ton	Hemp : 15 tons

The oak comes from the forests along the Atlantic coast of France, while the softwoods, including the Douglas Fir, come from the hills and mountains in the Eastern part of France. Masts and spars are made entirely of glued Douglas Fir wood from North America.

Searching in the Breton forest, using templates of the curved pieces to be found. Photos le Poupon
Photos Le Poupon (DR)

The complicated sawing of curved wood and checking the work with a template.

FRANCOIS ASSELIN
AND THE COMPANY BEARING HIS NAME

It is a local company specializing in the restoration of wooden structures in historic buildings which has up to the present secured the contracts for all the successive phases of the hull construction. Its great experience and skill with 18th century roofing structures is useful in the reconstruction of a frigate from the same period.

Having completed domes and arches, the company now works with the shipwrights on the curves of a ship.

As François Asselin says, "If the scarphed joints on beams are the same, the big difference between the static roof framing of a castle and the dynamic framing of a ship is that the latter has to be much more heavily reinforced and braced by curved pieces. Also, the water tightness is not ensured by a roofer but by the carpenter himself!" Joël Berthelot seeks out the crooked trees in the forests and Jacques Haie cuts them to shape for installation on the *Hermione*.

François Asselin (right) with his project leader, Jacques Haie (centre) pondering on the layout of a piece.

Damp-proof courses, traditional in shipbuilding to avoid rising damp by capillary action, are unknown in building framing. A fir peg, which will swell, is inserted into holes drilled in the assembly.

Views of the bow and stern of the **Hermione.** *Illustration by Dominique Gall.*

Her lower hull is sheathed in copper sheets to prevent barnacle fouling and to increase her speed.
Illustration by Jean-Benoît Héron.

Chapter V

The project of reconstructing the *Hermione*

Setting up a shipyard

The duration of construction

In 1807, the minister[1] issued a reminder of a regulation which had been forgotten during the revolution, stipulating that all frigates must remain at least two years in their construction docks, so that the framing would have time to dry out. Between the laying down of the keel and the launch, four or five years could sometimes elapse. The frigate *Vengeance* was completed in only 20 months, which was an unequalled record… except in the case of the *Hermione*, which was built as a matter of urgency in the unheard of time of 6 months !

Seasoned or green wood

In order to guarantee the quality of the construction and the longevity of the vessel, only dry, seasoned wood should be used in shipbuilding. But as there was very often insufficient seasoned timber available, the construction was deliberately slowed down to allow the wood to dry out gradually. The building of boats such as frigates was sometimes entrusted to private shipyards, like those of the Crucy brothers, who worked at Nantes, Lorient and Rochefort between 1793 and 1814. When these contractors put in their bids, they had to guarantee that they possessed a sufficient stock of seasoned wood. They had the right, however, to draw on the supplies of seasoned oak available in the navy dockyards, for a third of the timber required.

In 2006 the *Hermione's* shipyard was faced with the same problem of a lack of seasoned wood and therefore had to slow down the construction.

If a hull is covered with planking of green wood, these planks will dry out and shrink, leaving gaps too wide to be properly caulked. Oakum and caulking pitch cannot make up for the lack of wood and will not hold between insufficiently tight planks. Moreover, the sailors claimed that splinters of green wood were more dangerous than those of seasoned wood and they were therefore very watchful about the dryness of the wood.

Wood pits

In dockyards, the reserve stock of wood was very substantial, as 3 000 trees were needed for a ship of the line and there were dozens of ships to be built. While the trunks were

---

[1] Source : *Les Frères Crucy, entrepreneurs de constructons navales de guerre (1793-1814) Nantes, Lorient, Rochefort* by Yves Cossé.

waiting to be shaped and sawed, it was necessary to protect them against attacks by wood-boring insects, which particularly liked coniferous wood, above all when the bark was still on. Immersion of the wood in pits was always the solution adopted by the naval dockyards for the preservation of the timber reserves. An additional advantage was that wood which had had its sap washed, subsequently dried out much more quickly. The valley of the river Penfeld at Brest and the Scorff river at Lanester near to Lorient had pits of brackish water for both oak and masts. It would seem that Rochefort never had pits for the oak, but mast pits with a capacity of 1 200 masts were dug in 1668 and 1669 on the left bank[2].

1. *In 1786, the timber reserves at Rochefort were on the right bank close to the double graving dock and the mast pits were on the left bank opposite the roofed slipways. Model layout.*
2. *Pieces of oak forgotten for over a century in the Penfeld timber pits near Brest.*

The building slipways at Rochefort

Ships, including the *Hermione*, were built on gently sloping slipways going down to the water's edge and, when finished, they were launched by sliding. These docks were, so far as possible, sited facing north-south, so that the ship being built would not dry out more on the port side than on the starboard side. If the dock faced east-west, the side towards the sun would dry much more quickly and the ship would warp, taking on an irretrievable lateral arc.
The shipbuilding slipways were faced with stone and, in marshy zones or polders

[2] Down stream from Rochefort, in the parish of Saint-Nazaire.

such as Antwerp, Lorient or Rochefort, they were installed on a bed of driven piles or "in a more simple and economic manner, one merely resorted to laying down" a grid of horizontal beams pegged together to form an interlinked support distributing the pressure over the underlying mud. It was of course vital to avoid any risk of the dock distorting under the ever increasing weight[3] of the vessel under construction. On this raft base was installed a wooden ramp, whose incline was carefully calculated to allow the launching. The sliding force linked to the weight of the finished ship needed to be slightly greater than the frictional resistance. For ships of the line and

Three dimensional model of Rochefort, on which one can see ten slipways, four of which had roofs. The Hermione *was built in 1779 in one of these.*

frigates the slope was 1 in 12, for smaller craft it was 1 in 11 or 1 in 10. If it was incorrectly calculated, the boat remained stuck or gathered dangerous speed.

The slipway, which always remained dry, was prolonged at the river end by a submerged section which supported the hull until the ship was able to float. The launch was always undertaken at high tide, to limit the required length of the submerged section.

Cribbing (wooden block assemblies) adjusted the angle of incline of the future keel. There needed to be at least 1.20 metres clearance above the ground to allow workers to peg and caulk the planking adjacent to the keel.

---

[3] More than 1 200 tons for a frigate and several thousand tons for a ship of the line.

The covered slipways

As soon as it is launched, a ship starts to deteriorate. It is much better preserved beneath a shelter. Moreover, as the building of each ship usually took several years, the job was made easier if a roof protected the work piece and the dockyard workers from the sun and the rain.

Ships were therefore often built in covered slipways and laid up in them until the need arose for the Navy to call for them to be launched. So in times of peace there were in the dockyards a number of roofed slipways containing ships ready to be launched. Those on open slipways were protected by a light roof built on the ship itself.

Today the *Hermione* is being built inside a closed tent structure, equipped with an atomizing system to keep the timbers at the optimum hygrometric level.

The dry docks or graving docks at Rochefort

The first masonry dock was built at Rochefort in 1671 by François La Vau. This type of graving dock, called "French style" in France and "English style" elsewhere, permitted ship's hulls to be repaired, cleaned of fouling and re-caulked without having to lay the ship over on its side, which strains the structure and tires the sailors. Careening a ship involves unshipping the upper masts, disembarking the guns, and closing and sealing the gun ports. Rafts loaded with the ship's guns were used to heel the hull over, by pulling on the top of the lower masts.

The Louis XIV graving dock soon became insufficient for the activity of the port of Rochefort and it was decided to build a very innovative double dock (1683-1728) for the construction or refitting of two boats, one behind the other, separated by lock-type gates.

Covered slipway at Rochefort. Archives du Service historique de la Marine.

This double dock had stepped sides to allow easy circulation of workers round the ship and a convenient means of installing shoring props. Both the Louis XIV and the double dock gave onto the Charente river by means of a floating gate or "boat gate", which was fitted into grooves in the masonry. To open this gate, water was first let into the dock at high tide and then water was pumped out of the floating gate, which rose out of the retaining grooves and allowed free passage. These docks were equipped with pumping systems for both emptying them of water and coping with the numerous seepages from the river and the marshes.

Careening with breaming (burning off fouling) in the port of Bayonne in 1760.

Detail of a painting by Joseph Vernet.
Musée national de la Marine à Paris, photo par JMB.

It is in the riverside basin of the double dock that the *Hermione* is being reconstructed. She will be floated out by simply filling the basin and opening it onto the river. But it will first be necessary either to put the floating gate back into working order or to instal a lock.

A large new dock parallel to the double dock was built in 1853 under Napoleon III's Second Empire.

Upper left : The Louis XIV dock renovated and re-used : a fishing boat being cleaned and repaired in 1997. The arch on the side was part of the pumping system. Unlike its successor, it does not have stepped walls.

Lower left : The remains of the floating gate. Notice the groove in the masonry.

Right : the work-site is at the back, the structure covering the Hermione in the Louis XV double dock is on the left, with the shipwrights' shed just behind it. The stock of timber is stacked along the Napoleon III dock and the marquee containing the workshops of the blacksmiths, the sail makers and the carpenters is to the right.

In the background is the Charente river which will carry the frigate towards the sea. Photo AH.

The phases of the reconstruction : the framework

The framework of a ship and its longer, more slender form

The frame of a ship has invariably been compared to the skeleton of a mammal. It is certain that there is a close resemblance between the wooden ribs fixed to the keel and the bone ribs joining the spinal column. Until the time of the ship Saint Louis (1642) the keel was made out of a single tree trunk and the hull[4] was therefore very squat. The discovery of methods of joining trunks end to end meant that keel lengths were no longer restricted by the length of tree trunks. The lengthening of keels and consequently of ships gave greater capacities and increased sailing speed, owing to the changed length to beam ratio. This evolved from 2.5 for the Saint Louis to 3.7 for 18th century ships of the line, 3.8 for frigates and 3.9 for corvettes. As for merchant ships, the ratio would reach 5 to 7 for the late 19th century clippers, which represented the summit of the art of building wooden ships. They reached speeds of 14 to 15 knots, which was faster than steamers of the same period.

The keel and its assemblies

The assemblies

As the size of ships increased, it was necessary to find a way to join together several trunks to make up a long keel. The scarph joint used, called by the French "Jupiter's thunderbolt", as it has the shape of a lightning flash, had several variants, some of which are shown in the drawing by Fréminville.

Two vital precautions must be observed :
- the upper part of the joint must face towards the bows, so that if there is a violent shock the foremost piece can be ripped away without causing further, more serious damage. If it were placed the other way round, it would not be only one piece of wood that would be displaced, but two or more,
- "no joint must be placed beneath the foot of any mast, as the considerable pressure exerted by its own weight, as well as the forces applied by the rig, tend to distort the keel. If this thrust bore down on a joint, it would be liable to flex or break it and cause the most dangerous leaks."[5]

The various forms of scarph or hooked splice joints according to Fréminville.

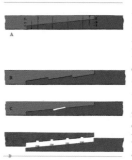

A : *pegged scarph joint, as used for the keel of the* Hermione, *held in place by 3 bronze clench bolts and two nails.*
B : : *stepped scarph joint, more difficult to make and often developing play after drying out.*
C : *keyed joint, which could be re-tightened with heavy blows with a sledgehammer before the ship's launch. The* Hermione's *deck beam clamps use this type.*
D : *joints with tongues and grooves or shallow tenons : the most recent form.*

Direction of disposing the joint.

YES

NO

Ship's bows to the left

---

[4] The hull of the Saint Louis was 25 m long by 10 m in the beam. 50 horses were embarked.
[5] *Traité pratique de construction navale (Practical treatise on naval construction)* by Fréminville.

1. *Hooked splice joint in the* Hermione's *keel.* Photo AH.   **2.** *Scarph joint in raised lip of the waterway around the decks.* Photo AH.

The keel

The keel is made up of three superposed layers (or 4, counting the keelson), held together by metal bolts. 12 large trees were therefore required for the Hermione's keel.
The false keel, attached to the underside of the keel, was designed to protect the keel and hull from any grounding and knocks. Its depth is equal to the thickness of the hull planking. Fixed to the keel by iron staples so that it could be torn off without inflicting damage on the keel itself, it is composed of five pieces scarphed together, any of which could be easily replaced if damaged.
The keel, made up of three pieces scarphed together, is the main structural component of the ship, its backbone. It has grooves, called rabbets, on each side all along its length, into which are inserted the edges of the garboard strake (the lowest tier of planking). This joint between keel and hull planking is one of the most difficult to make watertight.
The dead-wood, composed of four pieces, lies above the keel. The floor timbers are inserted into cut-out crenellations in the upper surface.

Illustration of the entire keel assembly, composed of 3 superposed parts

1a - *the dead-wood (or rising), notched to take the floor timbers and cross chocks, fitted side by side.*

1b - *the keel with the longitudinal grooves, the rabbets, for inserting the garboard strake.*
1c - *the false keel underneath, less deep.*

2 *The coupled floor timber and cross chock in place.*
3 *The assembly covered by the keelson, with cut-outs on its underside.*

Laying down the keel

The 1 200 ton weight of the finished ship will be borne by the keel and its cribbing, the supporting bed of tiered wooden blocks. It is vital that the ground be stable to avoid any distortion of the keel, which is initially very flexible, being long (40 m) and thin (38 cm wide). It is indeed as flexible as a one metre long strip of wood with a section of a centimetre.

1 -*Preparations for laying the keel began in June 1997 with the placing of perfectly aligned cribbing assemblies. These the bottom of the hull at least a metre above the floor so that the lowest strakes can be fitted and caulked.* Photo AH.

2 - *The parts of the keel ready for assembly with the forefoot knee front left.* AH, photo Pierre Talon.

3 - *The great day, the Fourth of July 1997. The laying of the keel, marking the* Hermione's *birth, takes place symbolica American Independence Day. The officials affix a souvenir plaque.* Photo AH.

4 - *The forefoot knee, the bottom of the stem, is lowered into place on the cribbing and attached to the keel, which is composed of three tree-trunks placed end to end. The keel is first assembled lying on its lower edge, then turned on its have the false keel nailed to it, before being returned to its final upright position. The stem will later be fitted to the up of the forefoot knee.* AH. Photo Pierre Talon.

The keelson

All the floor timbers are pinched between the keel and the keelson, which covers over the assembly.

Fitting of a length of the keelson. The floor timbers fit with precision into the slots on the underside. Photo AH.

The keelson, now fully fitted and extended in the foreground by the sternson, covers the floor timbers and strengthens the framing. Photo AH.

The stern-post

A more or less vertical timber to which the rudder will be attached. At its junction with the keel, it is strongly braced by the stern-post knee and the sternson.

Preparation of the stern-post, already slotted to take the transom beams of the stern frame, the equivalent of horizontal ribs. Photo AH.

The stern frame

The pronounced curve of the hull planks right at the stern of a boat and their fastening to the structure require a special framework known as the stern frame. The ribs can no longer be vertical and are therefore laid out horizontally. The topmost of these transom beams, the wing transom, is a very complex athwartship timber with a double curvature. The whole stern frame is assembled separately on the ground, as if it were a section of a boat under construction. The stern-post, laid flat like a keel, is fitted with the transom beams, the equivalent of ribs[6]. The whole assembly is then lifted to be fixed to the aft end of the keel and is held in place with shoring timbers. This system of construction with a stern frame gave ships square sterns, which resulted in a dead angle between the arcs of fire of the main batteries and the stern chaser guns. This gave rise to the development in the 19th century of rounded sterns, which were sturdier and permitted the chaser guns to fire obliquely.

An extraordinary piece of sculpture ; the stern frame seen from the left, with the stern-post flat on the ground in the middle. AH, photo Jean-Luc Moreau.

[6] But unlike the multi-component ribs, the transom beams are single pieces of wood let into the front face of the stern-post.

Moving into position the stern frame mounted onto the stern-post. AH, photo Bernard Henry.

① **②**

1. *Red letter day on August 20th 1997 : the stern frame and stern-post are placed on the aft end assembly of the keel, with the stern-post knee and the inner stern-post already fitted. The stern frame assembly of the* Hermione *is 7m high, 6.5m wide and weighs 6 tons.* AH, photo Bernard Henry

2. *The stern-most frame rib is fitted next to the stern frame. September 1997.* AH, photo Jean-Luc Billot.

The taffrail

The horseshoe shaped taffrail being fitted. Photo AH.   *How the taffrail looked several months later. Photo AH.*

Frame, ribs

As the section of the ship is very round, the ribs have to be cut out of very crooked pieces of timber. As scarphed joints are too weak and use up too much crooked wood, the technique of assembling ribs from two thicknesses of wood, laid side by side, was adopted. Short pieces of bent wood placed end to end make up the first rib. A second layer is added with the end joins carefully spaced in alternation with those of the first layer. The layers are then solidly pegged or bolted together.

The midship rib is the widest rib, situated half-way along the length of the ship. Its surface area is 57m² for a frigate and 104m² for a large ship of the line.

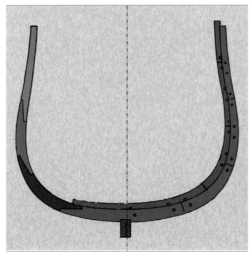 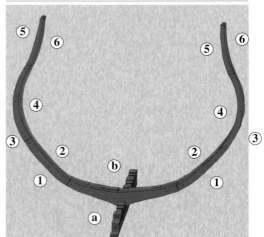

Diagram showing the different methods of making up a rib : left side with scarphed joints requiring large quantities of long crooked wood, right side with twin layers with offset joins. JMB d'après Fréminville.

Diagram keel and ribs.
*Floor timber (**a**), cross chock (**b**), lower or 1ˢᵗ futtocks (**1** and **2**), futtocks (**3** and **4**), top timbers providing tumblehome (**5** and **6**).*

The main ribs, known as principal timber, are put in place first and act as guides for the intermediate ribs.

The cant frames at bow and stern are not set up at right angles to the keel but run obliquely. They are perpendicular to the hull planking rather than to the keel, in order to follow the narrowing line towards the stem. This greatly reduced the work of angle shaping necessary and the section of the rib, instead of being diamond shaped, which was very wasteful of wood, could remain square.

Filling timbers were placed between the other ribs, if they were too widely spaced, partly to block penetration by canon balls (see section on ships' sides and canon balls on page 77).

The frame

The frame is the entire set of structural members and ribs of a ship. The first phase is to fit all the load-bearing frames and the second is to add all the filling timber, after which the vessel is considered "fully wooded".

The composition of a rib

- The floor timber is at the base of the rib and bears on the keel. It is symmetrical and has joined to it futtocks, attributed odd identification numbers.
- Two symmetrical futtocks and the cross chock, a shorter floor timber, form the base of the second lateral layer of the same rib. This is also extended by upper futtocks, bearing even identification numbers.
- The inward curving top-timbers produce the tumblehome, the narrowing of the hull as it comes up to the weather deck.

This method of framing was modified in the early 19th century to make more

economical use of curved wood. The floor timber became asymmetrical with unequal length arms, becoming shaped like a pipe. The cross chock disappeared and the second floor timber was turned around to give alternating arm lengths, thus providing the offsetting of the joins and the futtocks. So the two sides of a rib were almost identical but inversed and then fixed together.

The floor timbers were said to be "flat" in the centre part of the ship, "V-shaped" as they took on a more pronounced angle, while the tight angled ones right at bow and stern ends were known as crotches. The "flat" floor timbers in ships of the line in fact had a slight angle, while those in frigates had a steeper angle to make them less leewardly (losing ground by drifting downwind). This feature also adds slightly to their draught.

Shipwrights searched assiduously for forked oaks from which to cut crotches. But this single piece did not always prove to be as strong as was hoped, because the natural fork of a tree lacks cross fibres running between the two branches.

Large tree fork in Gâvre forest

Foresters are well aware that the crotches of forked trees often split apart when subjected to high winds.

So two-piece jointed crotches were made up with solid bracing called "wolf's paw". The ribs are cut out of crooked timber that is hard to find, particularly in large sizes such as those required for the *Hermione*.

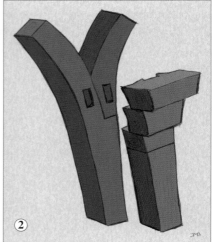

1 *A crotch in position.* Photo AH.

2 *Sketch of a jointed crotch with "wolf's paw" reinforcing assembly, in the absence of single piece crotches..*

3 *A "wolf's paw" assembly with two shipwrights proudly displaying their sculpture.* Photo AH.

The assembly of a rib

With the help of a plywood template, produced by the drawing office, the different pieces of the "first layer" of the rib are cut out with a jig-saw, trimmed, accurately angled[7] and fitted. The second layer is then laid alongside it and adjusted in the same manner. The two layers used to be pressed against one another by a "bridle" ("bridole" in French), made of rope checked with wooden wedges : modern screw presses are quicker and more efficient !

They were permanently fastened together with iron pins, hammered in after a pilot hole had been bored. Sometimes these pins were inserted obliquely, in opposite directions alternately, to avoid any risk of the pieces working loose.

---

[7] Angling consists of imparting a slight angle to the external face in relation to neighbouring ribs, so that the curved hull planking will lie perfectly flush against the ribs.

The finished rib, flat on the ground, was absolutely identical to the shape of the template. It was essential to ensure that it was not subsequently distorted by its own considerable weight and the operations of manoeuvring it into position. The distance between the arms was maintained by nailing on three cross-spalls (temporary distance pieces).

When a rib had been completed, it was used as a platform or workbench on top of which the next rib was assembled, because there was always a lack of space in the workshop area. In this way, stacks of four or five ribs were constituted, as near to the keel as possible. Some of them were laid flat on the keel itself and only needed to be raised into the vertical position.

Lifting and installing a rib

The finished rib, held in shape by the cross-spalls between the arms, could then be hoisted into its final position. This was a very delicate operation, as a completed rib, weighing nearly 1.7 tons, is made up of 14 heavy pieces of timber, very accurately assembled together. There was a risk of straining or weakening it.

Some of the largest ribs, particularly heavy, instead of being entirely made up on the ground, were installed in three stages. The assembled floor timbers and lower futtocks were fitted and then the two upper arms separately, one after the other.

In the drawing area, preparation of the plywood templates. Photo AH.

1. *Preparation of a rib on the assembly grid. Cross chock on top of long armed floor timber.*

2. *Placing of the lower futtock.*

3. *Drilling and insertion of a pin fastening together rib layers.*

4. *Detail of the dead-wood with cut-outs for the floor timber and cross chock forming the base of the twin-thickness rib. Beneath are visible the scarphed keel joint and the false keel on the cribbing.*

5. *Detail of the base of a rib, with the different width cut-outs in the bottom of the floor timber and the cross chock, fitting over the dead-wood.*

6. *Lowering a rib into position*

7. *For today's* Hermione, *the 5 ton travelling crane has greatly facilitated the installation of the frames.*

All photos AH.

(1)

Balancing, squaring and smoothing

Once the rib has been put in place, it must be accurately positioned and fastened symmetrically either side of the centre line and perfectly perpendicular to the keel in both planes.

The outer and inner faces must then be planed until all the ribs are perfectly aligned before the ceiling (inside planking) and hull strakes are fastened to them. The smoothing is guided, starting from the principal timber, by the use of ribbands (external wooden slats outlining the form of the ship at different levels and having the frame stations marked on them).

1. *Inwardly angled rib at the bows.* Photo AH.
2. *Planing into alignment the inner faces of the ribs before fitting the ceiling.* Photo Asselin.
3. *Plumb lines to check that ribs are perpendicular.* Photo AH.

(2)

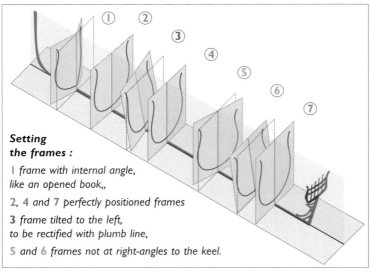

Setting the frames :

1 frame with internal angle, like an opened book,,

2, 4 and 7 perfectly positioned frames

3 frame tilted to the left, to be rectified with plumb line,

5 and 6 frames not at right-angles to the keel.

(3)

THE ORDER OF PROCEEDING IN THE SHIPYARD

Traditionally, the stern-post assembly with the stern frame was first fixed to the aft end of the keel and the stem to the forward end. Then the midship frame was the first rib installed, followed in turn by the principal timber ribs, the intermediate ribs and the filling timbers. For all of them, the front side was the one facing the midship frame and the reverse side the one facing the aft or forward end of the ship.

For the *Hermione* of today, the traditional order was modified and the 62 ribs were installed starting from the stern and working forwards in order. The accuracy of the drawings and the cutting out and assembly of the frames by modern methods allows this sequential installation using travelling cranes.

To avoid any distortion, the ribs are held in shape with temporary diagonal and horizontal cross-spalls. The latter appear to be ready to take the deck planking, but they will be replaced by the real beams for the three decks.

Here the ribs are being installed in order from the stern forwards. Because of this, short distance pieces placed between each one ensure that the ribs are parallel and make adjustment easier. Photos AH.

The beauty of the ribs at the stern, of the keelson and sternson on the right and the stern frame with its horizontal transom bars at the far end.

The stem

The stem is composed of two layers, the stem itself with the apron, a reinforcing timber, bolted to the after side of it. Both of these components are cut from crooked wood with scarphed joints offset from each other to avoid any weak points. This assembly is fixed to the upper end of the forefoot knee, of which the lower end is fixed to the forward end of the keel, as we have already seen. The forefoot knee requires a piece of crooked timber of very substantial scantling, which is very hard to find. It can be supplemented by the stemson, a knee shaped piece joining the forward end of the keelson to the apron. Lateral pieces, the knight-heads or bollard-timbers, are added on either side of the stem, acting as the last cant ribs to strengthen the fastening of the hull planking. Traditionally the stem, apron and knight-heads were all assembled, pegged and bolted together on the ground before being hoisted upright, fixed to the forefoot knee and held in position by shoring props. As on the keel, a grooved rabbet on the stem will take the ends of the hull strakes.

1 *Fitting of the assembled stem and apron to the forefoot knee at the end of the keel, October 2nd 1999* Photo AH.

2 *At the base of the stem, a stepped knuckle timber supports the bottom of the bow structure of hawse-pieces. The sharply canted bow ribs can also be seen.* Photo AH.

3 *Handsome staircase shaped carving, the mated port and starboard knuckle timbers ready to be fitted.* Photo AH.

The bow structure

1. *The bow structure seen from the outside. The ribbands show the lines of the hull strakes which will cover the hawse-pieces and the ribs.*

2. *The finished bow structure made up of hawse-pieces, seen from the inside.* Photos AH.

Like closed fingers or two palms of hands on either side of the stem and its knight-heads, the bow structure is composed of edge-jointed filling timbers. The hawse-pieces[8] seat onto an extraordinary carved piece, the forward knuckle timber. The bow will be finished off by the cut-water (see pages 86 and 87).

The breast-hooks

A kind of horizontal rider or knee, reinforcing the bow structure from the inside or supporting the ends of the decks. The vertical hawse-pieces, covered over by the hull planking, will be sandwiched between the breast-hooks and the cheeks of the head, both disposed horizontally.

One of the breast-hooks of the bow structure. This one, on the gun deck, will be level with the cheeks of the head on the cut-water on the outside of the bow structure. 4m long and weighing 980 kilos, it acts as a support for the bowsprit. Photo AH.

---

[8] The hawse-holes are two openings in the bow for the passage of the anchor cables. The edges are strengthened by softwood hawse-bolsters, thick pieces of plank called "naval hoods".

The skin of the ship

The planking

The skin of the ship, consisting of thick planks ensuring water-tightness, is fastened on to the framing ("laying on the skin"). The outside planks of the hull should be distinguished from the planking lining the inside of the hull, known as the ceiling and made up of foot-waling, clamps and thick-stuff. Wales, which are external  strakes of broader and thicker planks than the rest, reinforce the structure at several levels. The planks of the bottom, the wales, the thick-stuff and the ceiling were usually oak. The planks of the bottom were sometimes beech and those of the top-sides in softwoods, which weighed less. The garboard strake is the lowest strake, the edge of which is let into the rabbet, a longitudinal groove along the keel, cut with an adze. Similar rabbets in the stem and stern-post take the ends of the strakes.

Stretching along the outside of the finished framework, the ribbands are forerunners of the oak planking which will cover the hull and make it water-tight.

The thickness of the hull planking and the ceiling

The thickness of the outside planking goes from 15 to 25 mm for small hulls up to 320 mm for the largest 18th century ships of the line. The planks of the *Hermione*, in particular those of the bottom, are 74 mm thick, while her wales, clamps (thicker inboard planks just below the deck beams) and the thick-stuff placed between the floor-heads and the clamps are 162 mm thick. They are all of oak.

Bending the planks by steaming

The bending of the planks, formerly done by heating them directly above a fire, was later done by steaming. Two treatments are sometimes necessary for the more sharply curved planks. The very tight radius curves, particularly those at the stern, cannot be handled by bending and the planks have to be cut out of naturally crooked wood.

Bending hull planks by heating them. Taken from Duhamel du Monceau.

The steam chamber and the table with multiple jacks to bend the planks. 74 mm thick planks are steamed for three hours and 162 mm thick ones for five hours.

The planking is initially applied as openwork with alternate strakes, because the wood dries out, owing to the duration of the construction. The last strakes, to close up the hull planking, will only be laid shortly before the ship is launched.

The fastening of the outside planking

The planking is fastened onto the frame with very large bronze or iron nails and above all with large oak, lathe-turned pegs called tree-nails, which have the advantages of being lighter and not rusting. After a pilot hole is drilled, the tree-nail, coated with pitch, is driven in from the outside for a force fit holding the plank to the

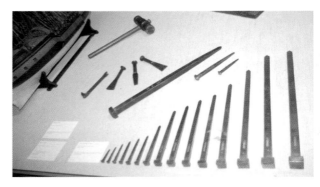

Set of nails for fastening the hull planking to the frame, forged at Romilly-sur-Andelle around 1810. Above, three iron ones : below, a series in copper from 6 to 60 cm long. Musée national de la Marine Paris, photo JMB.

frame. In some cases, split ended tree-nails go through the entire thickness of the ship's side and are held in place with a wedge driven into the end. On the *Hermione*, bronze nails are used, 135 mm long for the bulwarks, 178 mm long for the planks of the bottom and 270 mm long for the wales (see page 135).

Wooden tree-nails

The ceiling

The inside planking of the hull, fastened to the frame timbers with 178 mm or 270 mm nails, is called the ceiling. Thick-stuff (the term for all planking exceeding 4 inches, 102 mm, in thickness) covering the floor timbers or the futtocks, strengthens the hull longitudinally. It is linked to the outside planking by bolts passing through the floor timbers.

The ceiling is positioned and jointed with such accuracy that it forms a virtual second inboard hull.

View towards the stern, showing the fitting of the thick-stuff, providing longitudinal strengthening of the bottom of the hull. Photo AH.

The remainder of the ceiling planks are fitted, virtually making up a double hull. Notice the clamps, a row of thicker planks immediately below the deck beams.

The clamps

A row of thicker planks immediately below the decks, providing support for the deck beams.

THE SHIP'S SIDES : "ROOM AND SPACE" AND CANNONBALLS

The oak sides of a ship of the line can be up to 80 cm thick, including the outside planking, the frame timbers and the ceiling. The weak spots of this defence are the intervals left between a ship's timbers, known as "room and space", which may be between 3 to 6 cm. Naval instructions stipulated that the space should be less than the diameter of the cannonballs carried[9]. The sides were therefore reinforced at these weak spots by filling timbers between the main ribs, the spaces being even blocked out completely at the level of the gun decks.

On the *Hermione*, the sides were from 45 to 55 cm thick, depending on the zone, and the spaces between the ribs were from 9.5 to 10.5 cm. Her cannonballs were 12 cm in diameter (measured on the wreck).

1. *Detail of the* Hermione's *flank structure.*

2. *The "room and space" had to be less than the diameter of a cannonball. Note the double width of the space to lighten frigates.*

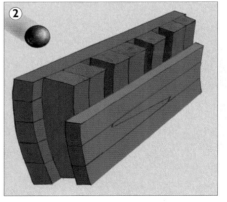

[9] Fréminville once again stated in 1864 "… so that a ball could never pass through a ship's side without encountering a frame timber which would offer such resistance as to attenuate its destructive effect."

Watertightness and protection

The caulking of the planking of the hull and decks

Jean-Luc Durand, caulker in action on the Hermione. *Photo AH.*

Caulking is the term used to designate the various operations required to make watertight the hull and the decks, the latter serving as the "roof" of the ship. Hemp tow, known as oakum, is first rammed hard into the seams between the planks. Traditional oakum consisted mainly of old ropes unravelled and teased apart and this was mixed with a form of putty. Hot melted pitch is then poured into the joins to seal them and to prevent the oakum from rotting. With 7 cm thick planks, at least three passages are required to fill the seams properly. In 2008 and 2009, the three decks were entirely planked and caulked. The hull surface, having been prepared and primed, now awaits its paint (see page 135).

Pitch

This resinous substance obtained by boiling is used for caulking and preventing the ingress of water. Mixed with tallow, it made a fatty tar used for waterproofing the topsides, the tarpaulins of the partners (frames round openings in the deck for masts, capstan and pumps) and protecting the hawsers and other cables.

Caulking the lower deck during 2009. The caulker uses a ladle to pour the hot pitch mixture into the seams of the orlop deck, already containing oakum. (photo AH SM).

Caulking the gun deck in mid-2009, using face-masks and equipment to ventilate the space and evacuate toxic fumes. See the finished result on page 119. (photo AH SM)

COPPER SHEATHING

To protect the planking from attack by shipworm, a first experimental solution was to add a sacrificial extra outer layer of ordinary planking fixed to the hull. This could be replaced in due course and did not adversely affect the robustness of the hull. Next was tried a system of covering the entire surface of the bottom with broad headed iron scupper-nails. Lastly was found the widely adopted solution of sheathing the bottom with copper plates. This had the additional advantage of greatly diminishing the fouling by seaweed, barnacles and other debris, which considerably slowed the ship. After a year's navigation a wooden bottom was festooned with a forest of marine plants which the crew tried to scrub off as best they could with hog brushes (called piglets in French), pulled by ropes.

The copper, covering the entire underwater surface, was laid in parallel lines onto a well scraped hull, smeared with pitch and tallow. The copper sheets were fastened on working forward from the stern to the bow and from the upper limit downwards, each sheet overlapping the previous one by several centimetres, like fish scales. They were held in place by copper sheathing nails to ensure that they did get torn off by the ship's progress through the water. The oxidation of the copper and the formation of verdigris protect the metal and its toxicity stops shellfish and seaweed from adhering to it. Copper sheathing increases the weight of the ship by one hundredth, but it increases its speed by 1/5th. Being very expensive, it increases the cost of the ship by about 20%. The British frigate *Alarm* was the first boat to be copper sheathed in 1761 and the practice started to be adopted in France in 1778. It was extended to all warships in the 19th century. The sheathing of the *Hermione* in November and December 1779 required 1 100 sheets of English copper, which was delivered laminated to the île de Ré. The replica will be as the original was when first launched, without sheathing.

1. *The damage caused by the boring of the shipworm.*

2. *Warship with copper sheathing.*
Musée national de la Marine Paris, photo JMB.

The decks and their planking

The greatest care was also devoted to the construction of the weather decks, the roof of the ship, subjected to sun and rain and needing to be watertight for the comfort of the crew. They were made of fir, except for the zones of the gun-decks subject to the movements of the trucks (wheels) of the gun carriages. These had to be in hard-wearing oak, as the recoils wore a millimetre off fir decks for every 8 or 9 shots ! However, the forecastle, quarter-deck and gun deck of our replica are of Douglas fir and the orlop deck is oak. The decks are carried by slightly arched deck-beams[10], which tie the two sides of the ship together. The beams are supported by the clamps running the length of the sides, the deck-beam hanging knees and stanchions, vertical pillars at around a third of the span. Stanchions with steps[11] enabled the sailors to pass from one deck to another when ladders and stairways had been removed during certain manoeuvres. The *Hermione*'s three levels of deck are, in ascending order, the orlop deck, the gun-deck (the main deck) and the quarter-deck and forecastle, with the open waist between them.

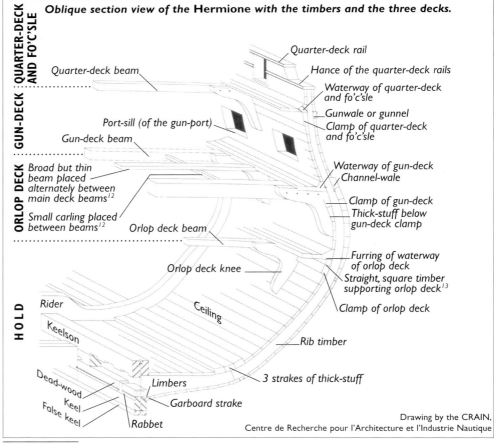

Oblique section view of the Hermione with the timbers and the three decks.

QUARTER-DECK AND FO'C'SLE

GUN-DECK

ORLOP DECK

HOLD

Quarter-deck rail

Hance of the quarter-deck rails

Waterway of quarter-deck and fo'c'sle

Gunwale or gunnel

Clamp of quarter-deck and fo'c'sle

Quarter-deck beam

Port-sill (of the gun-port)

Gun-deck beam

Waterway of gun-deck

Channel-wale

Broad but thin beam placed alternately between main deck beams[12]

Small carling placed between beams[12]

Orlop deck beam

Clamp of gun-deck

Thick-stuff below gun-deck clamp

Furring of waterway of orlop deck

Straight, square timber supporting orlop deck[13]

Orlop deck knee

Clamp of orlop deck

Rider

Keelson

Ceiling

Rib timber

Dead-wood

Limbers

3 strakes of thick-stuff

Keel

Garboard strake

False keel

Rabbet

Drawing by the CRAIN, Centre de Recherche pour l'Architecture et l'Industrie Nautique

---

[10] The slightly raised centre of the deck allowed rain and sea water to drain into the waterways and out through the scuppers.

[11] 8 cm deep notches at 30 cm intervals (see photos on pages 84 and 85).

[12] Items only found in French ships, with no particular name in English.

[13] Used in French ships where the English put lodging knees.

The gun-deck, recognizable by its gun-ports, is lit and ventilated, particularly during firing, by five gratings in the quarter-deck. Note the deck-beams and the hinged stanchions (posts). Seen from level of the large capstan. Below is the orlop deck where the crew slung their hammocks. *Photo AH.*

The quarter-deck with, in the foreground, its topsail sheet bits for working the sails, just aft of the main-mast.

Rigidity of the hull :
jointing and disjointing

Links and drilling

The assemblies of framing timbers were strengthened with very long metal bolts and pins. The holes were drilled only after the ship's frame had been finished. On frigates, the holes to be drilled could be as much as four metres deep in the stern-post structure and one can imagine the difficulty of the operation with the hand-drills and bits available at the time! The bolts were then driven in and clinched to ensure the tightness of the assembly and rigidify the ship.

Drilling an assembly of oak timbers. The longest were 2.95 m for the cut-water and 3.75 m for the stern-post.

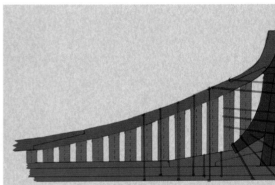

Sketch of the stern-post assembly.

Dangerous dislocation...

The operations of drilling and inserting the iron fastenings were very costly and were closely checked to avoid cheating when the construction of frigates had been contracted out to private shipyards. When a vessel started to become loose, sometimes after its very first service at sea, or if it had been strained by storms or weakened through old age, extra knees, riders and bolts were added. Among 74-gun ships, the *Suffren,* too hastily built at Nantes in 1804, or the *Regulus,* built at Lorient, needed to have strengthening timbers added at Brest. Many ships have foundered in storms, springing leaks in many places. The *Cygne* sank in this way on January 5th 1648 in the Gulf of Naples. A worse disaster occurred near Belle-Île when Admiral Tourville was returning with four ships including the *Sans Pareil* and the *Conquérant*. He had the guns taken down to the holds to lighten the top-sides and put strong ropes around the hulls as for leaky barrels, but to no avail, as both vessels foundered. Because of defective joints in the frames or corrosion of the metal fastenings, the hull planking became leaky.

Corrosion : iron or copper, but never iron and copper

As soon as a ship was put into the water, the ambient humidity and the tannin in the oak attacked the iron. The fastenings lost strength owing to the disintegration of the iron and the wood and the ship started to come apart. The bolts became so corroded that they could break in two at the interface between the two sides of a rib.

For this reason, early in the 19th century, iron bolts were fitted enclosed in sleeves of hardwood with no tannin. This contributed to the solidity and above all isolated the iron fastening from the tannin of the oak at its most fragile point, between the two side-by-side layers of the rib. After drilling pilot holes for the bolts, the assembled timbers were taken apart so that larger holes could be drilled exactly in the same axes to house the sleeves. The solid wooden cylinders were then inserted, the timbers were re-assembled, the sleeves were drilled and the bolts fitted inside.

As the iron used to hold the timbers together corroded rapidly, it was sometimes replaced by copper or bronze, above all when the ship had had its bottom copper sheathed. It was quickly discovered that iron fastenings and copper sheeting created positive and negative poles[14], thus accelerating the corrosion. The *Hermione*, with traditional iron fastenings, had this problem after being copper sheathed. She was therefore condemned to have a short, but brilliant, life. In the interest of durability, bronze bolts and nails have been used for the replica.

The rigidity of the hull, a perpetual struggle

The rigidity of the hull comes from the design of the ship's frame, keel and ribs, its build quality and from tightly laid and well caulked planking. It is reinforced by the ceiling, also tightly laid, and as watertight as the outside planking, thus acting like the third layer of a plywood sheet.

Laden or in ballast (unladen) under sail, heeling on one tack and then on the other, the hull works and suffers, without mentioning the gales which shake it in every direction.

The progressive lengthening of hulls as time went on increased the number of frame timbers and worsened the problems of rigidity in ships subject to very high strains. So the quality of construction and of all jointing was ever more important. Ships, like houses, have different levels, supported by beams and vertical stanchions or pillars and this internal structure can be distorted like an un-triangulated diamond (later in the 19th century diagonal bracing was developed to triangulate and stiffen the hull[15]). In addition to the hanging knees, the waterways were fitted, longitudinal reinforcements serving the double purpose of providing a robust oak belt strengthening the join between the ship's side and the deck and of collecting the water on the decks and draining it off through the scuppers. This form of valley was also well suited to the trucks of the gun carriages, as the guns had to be run out as far as possible to increase firing angles.

---

[14] Electrolysis with sea water.
[15] Arman system in France, see Fréminville, Snodgrass in England.

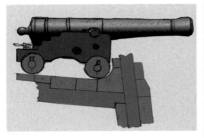

The waterway, reinforcing belt, had a shape which suited the gun trucks.

Fitting a waterway
Photo AH.

The waterway, here the one on the gun-deck, had scupper holes for draining water, as it was vital to keep the deck dry.
Photo AH.

Pillars in the hold : the first and second have steps cut in them, the third has side braces

In the centre, a rider with six limber holes for taking the bilge water to the pumps.

The riders

The finished hold, showing the 5 riders, thick, banana-shaped ribs, mounted over the ceiling and the keelson. Note the thick-stuff of the foot-waling with limber holes and channels for getting water to the bilge-pumps.

These kinds of floor timbers and ribs added above the ceiling make a fourth layer. As the keelson is twice as thick as the original one, the riders have had to follow, taking on a rather complicated hump-backed shape. Lastly, wedges or keys are hammered into the spaces between the ribs to block them in position and tighten them, increasing the rigidity still further. The whole hull is therefore "pressure-braced", but it will only remain tight if the bolts and fastenings resist corrosion.

The rider farthest forward. The twinned side-by-side timbers and their manner of assembly, just like the ribs, can be seen. Front right, a pillar with steps, 8 cm deep and 30 cm apart, for the sailors to climb when ladders or stairs have been removed.

To finish off the hull, the head or cut-water

Once the hull has been finished and planked, the bow will be extended by the knee of the head[16], which will support the bowsprit and the forestays of the masts. The top of the cut-water, right at the forward tip of the prow, is decorated with gilding and the figurehead, a lion in the *Hermione*'s case.

The head comprises two parts.

The first part is the longitudinal centre-line timber continuing forward from the false keel. It is made up of multiple pieces which are joined together and to the stem by mortises and tenons. The standard knee fastens the cut-water to the stem and serves as a hook for attaching the main-mast forestays.

The second part buttresses the first against lateral pull, by the cheeks of the head and the rails of the head, which run across the bow as far as the cat-heads. On this structure is laid the duckboard flooring of the head on each side of the stem "for the private use of the sailors", washed down by the waves and the spray. The conveniences of the officers were in the quarter-galleries at the stern.

The bowsprit is attached to the cut-water by lashings passing through holes called cats' paws. Bob-stays underneath, attached to the stem, counteracted the upward pull of the rigging.

Sketch of the details of building up the head (see fitting of the head on page 134)

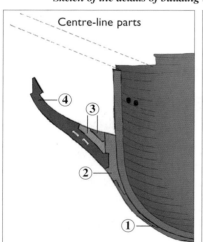 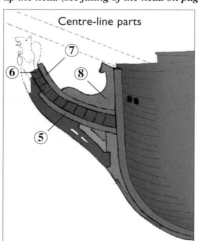 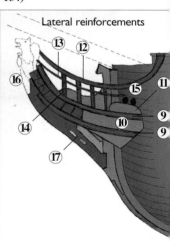

Centre-line parts

1. *Fitting the gripe to the forward end of the false keel.*

2. *The heel of the knee of the head*

3. *Upper, inner part of knee of the head*

4. *The cut-water*

5. *Lower triangular piece filling up the angle of the knee of the head[17]*

6. *The trailboard*

7. *Upper triangular piece filling up the angle of the knee of the head[17]*

8. *The standard, fastening cut-water to stem*

Lateral reinforcements

9. *Cheeks of the head*

10. *Filling timbers between the cheeks*

11. *Hawse-bolsters or naval hoods*

12. *Large rail of the head*

13. *Small rail of the head*

14. *Vertical bars*

15. *Hawse holes*

16. *Figurehead*

17. *Cats' paws*

---

[16] Giving the prow a snake-like profile. Many centuries earlier, Viking longships had prows topped with snake or dragon heads to terrify the enemy.

[17] Items only found in French ships, with no particular name in English.

1/18th scale model of the Hermione *by Jean Thomas : the cheeks of the head have just been fitted.*
Photo Jean Thomas.

1/36th scale model of the Hermione *by Jean-Claude Cossais : details of the finished head.*

1/18th scale model of the Hermione *by Jean Thomas : the head almost finished with its figurehead. The large rail is being held in position.*

Masts and spars

A sailor is on look-out duty on the main top. Topmen are climbing up the ratlines of the shrouds of the main-mast and another is on the shroud ratlines of the main-top-mast towards the main-top-gallant-mast.

Mizzen-mast	Main-mast	Fore-mast
Mizzen-top-gallant-mast	Main-top-gallant-mast	Fore-top-gallant-mast
Mizzen-top-mast	Main-top-mast	Fore-top-mast
Lower-mizzen-mast	Lower-main-mast	Lower-fore-mast

Quarter-deck and forecastle

From the stern going forwards : hen-coops, the wheel with the helmsman and an officer, the mizzen-mast, the stairs for commissioned officers, the main-mast, the piled up ship's boats, the fore capstan and the fore-mast.

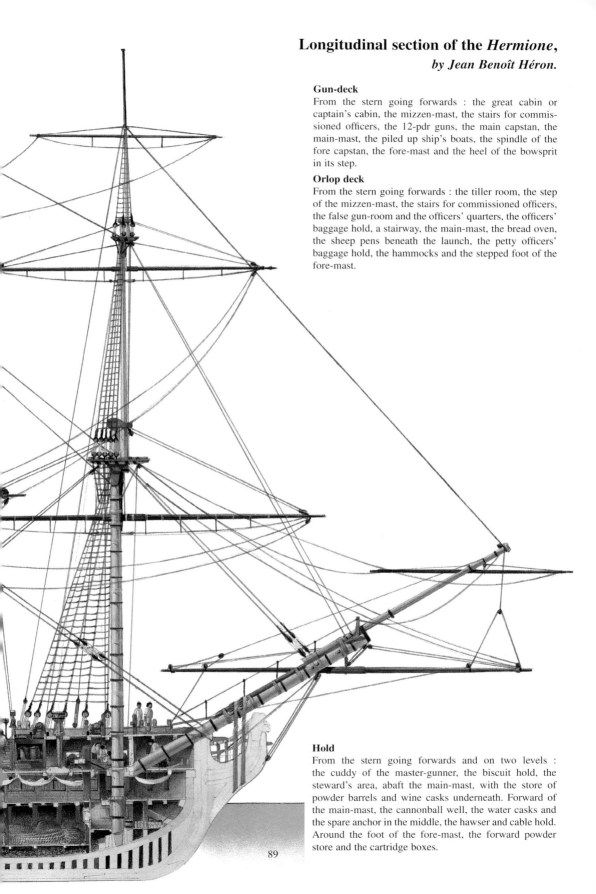

Longitudinal section of the *Hermione*, *by Jean Benoît Héron.*

Gun-deck

From the stern going forwards : the great cabin or captain's cabin, the mizzen-mast, the stairs for commissioned officers, the 12-pdr guns, the main capstan, the main-mast, the piled up ship's boats, the spindle of the fore capstan, the fore-mast and the heel of the bowsprit in its step.

Orlop deck

From the stern going forwards : the tiller room, the step of the mizzen-mast, the stairs for commissioned officers, the false gun-room and the officers' quarters, the officers' baggage hold, a stairway, the main-mast, the bread oven, the sheep pens beneath the launch, the petty officers' baggage hold, the hammocks and the stepped foot of the fore-mast.

Hold

From the stern going forwards and on two levels : the cuddy of the master-gunner, the biscuit hold, the steward's area, abaft the main-mast, with the store of powder barrels and wine casks underneath. Forward of the main-mast, the cannonball well, the water casks and the spare anchor in the middle, the hawser and cable hold. Around the foot of the fore-mast, the forward powder store and the cartridge boxes.

Transversal section of the *Hermione*, *by Jean Benoît Héron.*

LEVEL WITH THE FORE-MAST

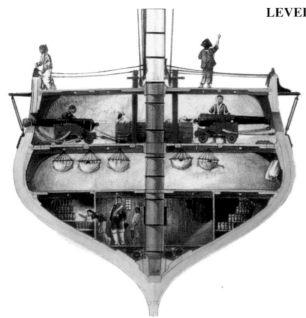

Forecastle : the deck for working the fore-mast and the bowsprit, with the fore capstan on the aft part of it. It might have two to four 6-pdrs mounted on it. A boatswain in a three-cornered hat is giving his orders.

Gun-deck : carrying 12-pdr guns, the largest on the frigate. The gun on the right is run in and the one on the left is run out. The cannonballs are in the shot racks under their muzzles.

Orlop deck : a man could hardly stand upright. Five sailors are resting in their hammocks. Their bags contain their changes of clothes.

Hold : two men and a powder monkey have come to the powder store to fetch cartridges. Four old cannons in the bilges act as ballast

LEVEL WITH THE MAIN-MAST

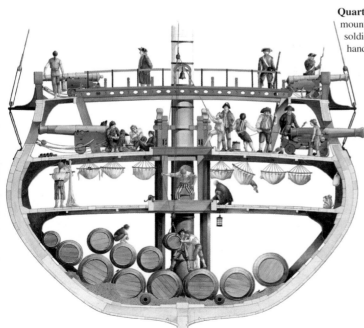

Quarter-deck : the officers' deck, with 6-pdrs mounted. One can see a single officer, two armed soldiers and a gunner with a powder cartridge in his hand. Outside the bulwarks, the chain-wales, broad horizontal planks, prevent the shrouds from rubbing against the gun-wale. Below them are the shroud chains fixed to the hull and above them are pairs of dead-eyes.

Gun-deck : carrying 12-pdr guns. The gun on the left is run in and the cannonballs can be seen in the shot rack under its muzzle. Four sailors are eating from a common dish. On the other side, three gunners and a ship's boy, cartridge in hand, are running out the gun. One of the gunners holds the hand-crow-lever used to move and point the heavy gun and the other the lint-stock. Master gunners and boatswains can be recognized by their three-cornered hats.

Orlop deck : eight sailors are resting in their hammocks and another is slinging his. A cat shares with the ship's boys the vital task of chasing rats.

Hold : through a kind of well passing through the decks, the sailors are manhandling a barrel. A load of barrels held in place in a bed of sand and two old cannons in the bilges act as ballast. The cargo must always be carefully wedged to prevent it shifting when the ship heels, as this could cause it to capsize.

Chapter VI

The fitting-out and armament of the frigate

The masts and yards

Masts and yards	LENGTH IN M	MAX DIAMETER IN CM	WEIGHT IN KILOS
Bowsprit (with jib-boom)	16.25	67.7	1 300
Fore-mast, overall height	54		
Lower fore-mast	24.40	67.5	3 050
Fore-top-mast	16.9	40.6	1 200
Fore-top-gallant-mast	12.7		
Main-mast, overall height	56.55[1]		
Lower-main-mast	27.07	70.4	3 400
Main-top-mast	16.9	40.6	1 200
Main-top-gallant-mast	13		
Mizzen-mast, overall height	35		
Lower-mizzen-mast	16.60	40.3	740
Mizzen-top-mast	11.4		
Mizzen-top-gallant-mast	8.9		
Yards			
Fore-yard	23.4	48	1 150
Main-yard	25.5	55.4	1 525
Mizzen yard	23.7	40.5	960
Fore-top-gallant yard	11		80

The bowsprit rests on the top end of the stem, passes through an intermediate support plate and its heel is held fast in a substantial step. Photo AH.

The bowsprit

A large boom projecting over the stem, rising between 25 and 35° above the horizontal plane – the *Hermione*'s is at 30°. The bowsprit was originally considered to be the most forward mast on a ship and of crucial importance, as the forward stays maintaining the other masts were attached to it and it enabled jibs to be carried. To resist the considerable pull exerted on it, the bowsprit was securely embedded in the hull and held by lashings, a bob-stay and shrouds. Extended by a jib-boom, in the same manner as a top-mast on a mast, it has an overall length of 16.25 m, taking the total length of the *Hermione* to 65 m.

---

[1] Of which 45m is above the quarter-deck.

(1) (2) (3) (4)   **Firs   Pines**

Comparison of different masts :
1. *The* Royal-Louis, *1690*
2. *The* Montebello, *1814*
3. *The* Hermione, *1779 and 2000*
4. *The* Recouvrance. *1817 and 1992.*

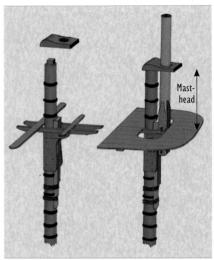

"Telescopic" masts

The tallest trees do not reach the height of the largest masts, up to 80 metres. Masts were therefore made up of 3 or 4 component masts, superposed and with sliding joins. The top, with its coaked fishes, cross-trees and cap, permits the top masts to be hoisted when the ship is at sea and to be lowered out of harm's way when the ship is inactive. A system of hoists and pulleys is used to sway up the masts and a wooden or iron bar called a fid then blocks them in position. The top-rope is the halyard used for this operation.

The mast-head cap

A block of elm or oak with iron straps set on top of a lower mast with a deep square mortise. The top-mast is drawn up through a round hole forward of the mortise. The top-gallant mast slides up through the cap of the top-mast in the same fashion.

Device for joining the masts with mast-cap and cross-trees

The mast-cap, the principal piece in the assembly of the masts, guides and secures the sliding upper mast.

The cap of the fore-top-mast from the wreck of the **Juste**, *a 74-gun ship built in Rochefort in 1724.*

Left : the hat-shaped upper side with the round hole through which the fore-top-gallant-mast was drawn up. Right : lower side with square mortise for insertion of the top of the fore-top-mast and eye-bolts for attaching the yard lifts and to take the hooks of the top-rope blocks.
Musée national de la Marine à Paris, photo JMB.

The lower mast, a 'made-mast'

The size of the lower mast made it necessary to assemble it, using several tree-trunks. This is known as a made-mast, as opposed to a pole-mast, made of a single tree. The spindle, a central trunk placed upside down, is surrounded by thinner timber, the side-trees and side-fishes, all of which are secured by strong iron hoops, heat-shrunk on to the mast.

The mast-head

The upper part of the mast, between the trestle-trees and the cap. The length of the overlap with the top-mast is around a seventh of the total length of the lower mast.

The sources of supply of the masts
Mast tracks

Ships without masts did not exist and the need for hull timber was accompanied by a need for timber for spars, from coniferous trees in the mountains or from northern Europe, especially slow growing Scots pines.

Previously, the main supply of mast timber had consisted of Scots pines from northern Europe and Russia, obtained through mast-brokers at the Baltic port of Riga. For reasons of French strategic independence, Louis XIV preferred to obtain fir trees from the Pyrenees (see photo page 145). After the Issaux forest had been exhausted, huge work was undertaken to create extraordinary "mast tracks", parts of which were hacked out of the vertical sides of mountain barriers, such as the Sescoue, to bring down forty metre long trunks from the Pacq forest.

As Corsica also had fine forests of large Corsican pines (P.nigra maritima) suitable for masts, Louis XV bought the entire island from the Genoese, at the urging of his Navy Minister, the duc de Choiseul, in order to satisfy the navy's needs for mast timber.

Mast track in the Aspe valley (Pyrenees).

THE HERMIONE, MASTS OF YESTERDAY AND TODAY

As the forests of the Pyrenees had been virtually exhausted by 1779, the masts of the original *Hermione* may have come from Corsica but more probably from international merchants in Riga or elsewhere in the Baltic.

Those of today's *Hermione* are of Douglas Fir, whose wood is known commercially as Oregon pine. Unlike the originals, they are not made of entire trunks, but are glued assemblies, made up by modern methods which ensure a good compromise between historical appearance and improved stability and longevity.

The rigging

General term covering all the ropes and pulleys constituting the standing rigging (the shrouds, stays and braces which support the masts) and the running rigging (the halyards, sheets, clew-lines, etc. used in the management of the sails). To rig a ship is to sway up the masts, fix the yards to them and to attach all the components of the rigging.

The main-mast partner in the Hermione'*s orlop deck, seen from the hold. 4 semi-circular cut-outs on the partner's perimeter are for the tubes of the pumps.*

Likewise, on the model by Jean Thomas, the main-mast partner in the gun-deck with the 4 well-pump tubes.

Photo Jean Thomas.

The partners and the steps

Before being sustained by the fore and back stays and the shrouds, the masts are held by the partners, oak frames fitted in the apertures in the decks for the passage of the masts, and by the steps, large pieces of oak encasing the heels of the masts. The steps of the main-mast and fore-mast are fixed to the keelson, while that of the mizzen mast is fixed to the frame of the orlop deck (see illustration page 88). The partners are longer than they are broad, to allow for trimming the rake of the masts, which are then held in the desired position by wedges.

The stays

The masts are supported from the fore part of the ship by several stays, strong ropes which also carry the jibs and stay-sails. These are "set up" (tightened) by means of a

Detail of the stays and shrouds of the Royal Louis, *a 3-decker man of war built in 1759, 1/18th scale model. "Hearts" (see text) can be seen far left, attached to the mid-length of the bowsprit, and (centre) just in front of the mast, attached to the hook of the standard knee. Lashings holding down the bowsprit pass through "cat's paw" slots in the cut-water.*
Musée national de la Marine à Paris, photo JMB.

kind of dead-eye known as a "heart", a flattish round block with a single large hole. Straps (ropes spliced into a circular wreath) fit into a groove around the outside of the block and are attached to the standard knee of the head, the bowsprit or the foot of a mast farther forward. The lanyard of the stay is wound several times through the eye of the heart and is stretched as stiff as possible by the application of tackles.

The shrouds

A range of large ropes (today steel cables) extended from the mast-heads to chain-wales on the sides of the ship slightly aft of the mast, to give lateral support to the masts and counteract the forward pull of the sails. Shrouds are made of one piece of doubled rope fastened together in the middle to form a collar that is reeved to the

mast-head. The lower ends are fitted with dead-eyes, linked by lanyards to lower dead-eyes just above the chain-wales, below which the shroud chains are fixed to the ship's sides. The shrouds are denominated from the masts to which they belong, main, fore and mizzen shrouds, main-top-mast shrouds, main-top-gallant shrouds, etc. Frigates usually had 10 lower mast shrouds per side for each mast. The ratlines (or ratlings), small lines stretched horizontally across the shrouds, provide ladders on which the topmen can go aloft.

The cat-harpings of the centre shrouds brace them together behind the yards and provide

Another detail from same model. Chain-wales with shroud chains below and pairs of dead-eyes above.
Musée national de la Marine à Paris, photo JMB.

the anchorage point for the foot-hook shrouds running up to the edge of the top and bracing the top-mast shrouds. The port and starboard cat-harpings are linked by a lashing running between them.

Sometimes cat-harpings are dispensed with and the foot-hook shrouds of the top-mast are fixed directly to the lower mast below the cheeks.

The breast back-stays

Long ropes from the mast-heads of top-masts and top-gallant masts to their own chain-wales on the ship's sides, designed to support the upper masts, particularly in a fresh wind from the weather beam (after-back-stays do the same when the wind is aft). Each top-mast and top-gallant mast had one breast-back-stay per side.

The top and the fixing of the top-masts

The stable support of the lower masts is achieved by the wide spread of the shroud bases, the width of the deck plus the lateral projection of the chain-wales. In the same way, the "top", the platform fitted to the head of the lower mast, serves as a base for the top-mast shrouds. Its width being nearly half the length of the midship deck beam, it acts like a deck of reduced size. The topmen can rest on it and swivel guns can be mounted on pedestals on it during combat. It was round until the reign of Louis XV and then became square to increase the usable width. A rail with netting is supported by stanchions. The height of the rails on the *Hermione* has been increased in line with modern safety regulations. The main and fore tops are 5.4 by 5.7 m, while the mizzen top is smaller (3 x 3.2 m).

Constructing the top. Traditionally the knees and the rim of the top were oak and the planking was softwood for lightness. For greater durability, the tops of the replica have been made of heavier iroko. Photo AH.

The breadth of the top allows the top-mast shrouds to have a wide footing. The stanchions made in the shipyard forge support the guard rail for the topmen. Photo AH.

The lower dead-eyes of the top-mast shrouds are fitted with foot-hook plates which pass through holes in the edge of the top. Underneath, the foot-hook shrouds hooked into the lower ends of these plates run down to the cat-harpings, equalising the tension of the top-mast shrouds.

An aperture in the middle of the top, known as "the lubber's hole"[2], allows the passage of the top of the lower mast, of the foot of the top-mast and also that of the sailors. To reinforce the top, small knees radiate from the centre towards the rim.

Forward of the top, the crow-foot, a set of small cords fanning out from the stay, prevented the top-sail from getting worn by rubbing against the rim of the top or being caught under it.

The top-gallant masts

The base of their shrouds is not spread by a top, which would be too heavy, but by simple cross-trees, comparable to the shroud spreaders used on sailing yachts since the start of the 20th century. Lightness is always sought aloft.

---

[2] Lubber : contemptuous term for clumsy seaman. Use of lubber's hole avoided climbing overhung foot hook (or futtock) shrouds.

Making masts today

All the upper masts, including the top-masts set above the lower fore, main and mizzen masts and the top-gallant-masts above them at the top of the structure, were originally fashioned from single pine trunks (see drawing and table of mast positions pages 88 and 89). To ensure greater durability, today's masts are made of glued pieces of Douglas Fir, assembled end to end using the modern technique of cleft and wedge joints.

Detail of the assembled pieces of Douglas Fir. The interlocking teeth of the "spliced" cleft joint are just next to the sheave of a yard halyard, but they are so neat that they are almost invisible.

1. *The heel of a top-mast equipped with its bronze sheave for the top-rope to sway up (hoist) the mast (see page 92). The copper lined rectangular hole is for the insertion of a fid, a bar to block the hoisted mast in position.*

2. *The fixing together of a lower-mast and its top-mast by means of the mast-head cap (see page 92)* (photo AH SM).

3. *Two top-masts with their lower hoisting sheaves and two fully prepared yards (right of photo).*

The yards

Long pieces of timber to carry the sails. Yards are either square, carrying square sails, and suspended across the masts at right angles, or lateen, carrying triangular or trapezoid sails, and rigged obliquely. The yards of frigates, made from a single fir or pine trunk[3], were of round or octagonal section, tapering from the middle (the slings) towards the yard-arms (outer ends). Yards and sails derive their names from the masts to which they are attached, e.g. main-top-sail yard.

The cross-jack yard, the lowest square yard on the mizzen-mast, does not carry any sail, its arms serving to attach the clews (the lower corners) of the mizzen-topsail.

A number of ropes are needed to work the yards :

- jears, a set of tackles to hoist the lower yards into position,

- trusses, holding yards close to the mast, but allowing them to be trimmed round,

- lifts, running from the mast-head caps to pulleys above the yard-arms to sustain the yards and keep them horizontal,

- braces, fastened to the yard-arms to traverse the sails according to wind direction,

- brails, all the ropes (clew-lines, bunt-lines, leech-lines) for drawing the sails up to the yards, ready for furling,

The yard is attached to the mast by a parral, a collar with ribs and trucks (sort of wooden ball-bearing), enabling the yard to slide easily up or down the mast.

To give the topmen a foothold while loosening or furling the sail, a rope called a horse runs along below the yard. The horse passes through eyes in the lower ends of stirrups, short ropes nailed round the yards. Some yards have studding-sail booms, long poles sliding through boom-irons at the yard-arms. These are run out to spread the studding sails, additional lateral sails hoisted in moderate and steady following breezes.

Sli... (mid...

First yard ... the Hermio... made up of ... pieces of woo... 11 m long, it w... weigh 80 kg. T... yard-arms have to be finished.

Yards and the extraordinary web of shrouds and stays. On the main-top are four swivel guns for preparing the boarding of an enemy ship. They are mounted on pedestals made from small knees of crooked wood.Musée national de la Marine à Paris, photo Jean Boudriot.

[3] Over 25 m long for the main-yard of the Hermione. The yards for large ships of the line, up to 36 m long for a 120-gun 1st Rate, were assembled from several trunks.

Racks, bitts and kevels

On the orlop deck, beneath the gun-deck, the base of the main-topsail sheet bitts, a beautiful lyre shape forward of the main-mast, which will support the main rack. On the left, the foot of the knight-head for the lower jears.

1. *The large main-mast jear knight-head will be fitted with four sheaves. Chocks prevent any warping in the meanwhile.*

2. *On the forecastle, two racks for the fore-mast, bitts for blocks and swivel-hook block-straps. They have been drilled to take belaying pins.*

3. *The belaying pins will be placed on the racks at the foot of the masts to belay (fasten) the halyards.*

All these ropes for working the yards and sails will pass through systems of pulleys and be belayed to racks fitted with lathe-turned ash belaying pins.

Knight-heads, bitts and swivelling block racks…

On the gun-deck the large main-mast knight-head with its sheaves relays to the capstan the top-ropes for swaying up the heavy upper masts and the halyards of the main-mast yards.

Aft of the fore-mast, the large cable bitt has the anchor cable passed around it. Smaller topsail-sheet bitts or kevels, some of which are fitted with swivel-hook block-straps, have holes to receive belaying pins to fasten any part of the running rigging.

The large main-mast knight-head (see previous page), finished, painted red and fitted with its bronze sheaves. Behind it is the main capstan and the capstan levers can be seen on the deck on the right.

On the forecastle deck, from left to right on the photo (from aft going forward), the galley (kitchen) roof panel, the fore capstan with 2 pawls at its base and its levers on the deck behind it, the rack fitted with swivelling blocks but not yet equipped with belaying pins, the fore-mast knight-head, a square plate on the deck covering the partners for stepping the fore-mast and a forward rack with sheaves in the foot of the posts.

The large cable bitt is used to fasten and manoeuvre the very thick and heavy anchor cable. It consists of two vertical bitts and a massive oak cross-piece parallel to the deck. Forwards of it (on left of photo) can be seen the foot of the fore-mast knight-head and the very sturdy vertical oak timbers securing the heel of the bowsprit. The hole where the bowsprit emerges from the bow is visible (circle of light). In the foreground, the slightly conical vertical red column is the barrel or spindle of the fore (or jear) capstan, planted in its step and passing through its 'partners' (surrounding frame in the forecastle deck).

Rigging,

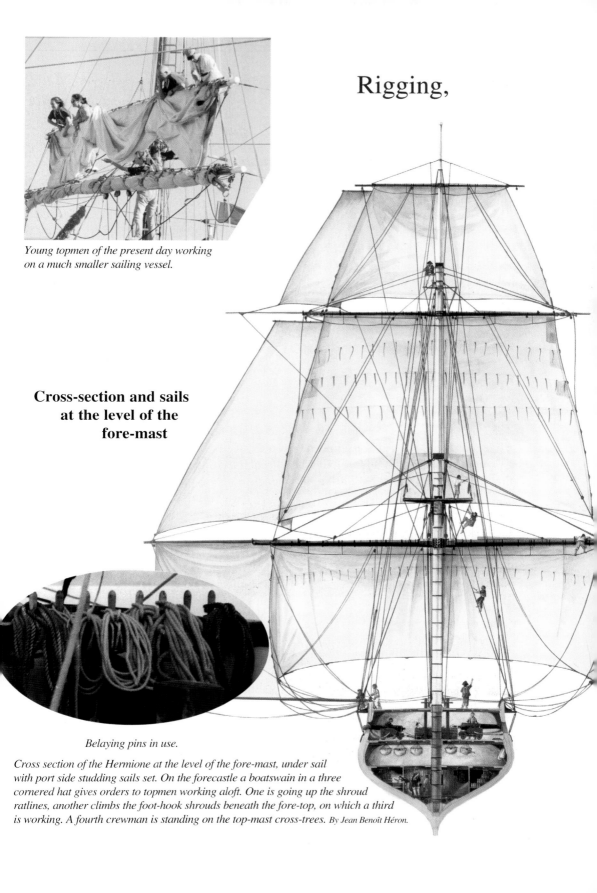

Young topmen of the present day working on a much smaller sailing vessel.

Cross-section and sails at the level of the fore-mast

Belaying pins in use.

Cross section of the Hermione at the level of the fore-mast, under sail with port side studding sails set. On the forecastle a boatswain in a three cornered hat gives orders to topmen working aloft. One is going up the shroud ratlines, another climbs the foot-hook shrouds beneath the fore-top, on which a third is working. A fourth crewman is standing on the top-mast cross-trees. By Jean Benoît Héron.

Fittings : ropes, blocks, sails, capstans, long-boat, pinnace and jolly-boat

The royal rope factory and cable lengths

Rope laying, drawing from the work of Duhamel du Monceau "La Fabrique des manoeuvres pour les vaisseaux ou l'art de la corderie perfectionné", 1769.

After a long voyage, the sailors were glad to see land again : at a few cable lengths from the shore, the anchor could be dropped. But what was a cable length, a term frequently used in the age of sail? The French used the span of the extended arms, the "brasse" and the standard length of anchor cables was 120 brasses. In England and in other countries, fathoms (6 feet) were the unit of measurement for cables and rigging and for depth sounding. The standard cable was 120 fathoms. The cable's length seems to have varied from one country to another[4].

Rope factories were housed in very long buildings, as making up a rope involved "laying" or "closing" together several strands of spun hemp. The twisting together of the strands shortens the final length of the finished rope. Making a hawser of one cable's length will therefore need a 300 or 400 m long building. That is why the rope factory at Rochefort is 372 m long and 8 m wide. The one at Toulon was of similar length but had three bays side by side for making three cables at the same time.

At the Rochefort rope factory, Mr de Fontainieu, Director of the Centre International de la Mer, sitting on an anchor cable 13.5 cm in diameter, comparable to those of the Hermione. *It is a stream-cable consisting of 3 hawsers, each having 3 to 6 strands.*

On the first floor, the skeins of hemp fibre were prepared and spun into rope yarn. Two, three or four rope yarns were warped together

---

[4] 120 French "brasses" (1.62 m) make a cable length of 195 m. 120 English fathoms (1.83 m) make a cable length of 220 m.

to make strands. Hawser-laid ropes were made of three strands, whereas cable-laid ropes were composed of three twisted hawser ropes. Laying was done by means of a grooved wooden cone, called the top, having the same number of grooves as there are strands to be closed together. Once the rope was finished, it was coated with tar to make it rot-proof.

The top, a grooved cone to lay the ropes. Here, four strands around a thin heart (middle strand) will make a hawser-laid rope. Corderie de Rochefort.

Sets of ready prepared gun-tackle for the cannons. Two will be required for each gun.

A sailor in the Corderie Royale undertaking various splicing operations for the Hermione. *He is attaching a cannon ball encased in leather thongs which will serve as a counter-weight for the bilge-pumps (see under pumps further on)* (photo AH SM).

Bull's-eyes

Blocks and dead-eyes

All the parts above the decks and participating in the operation of the rigging constitute the fittings of the superstructure. The hearts[5], bull's-eyes, dead-eyes, racks and belaying pins are made in the *Hermione* shipyard workshops. The sheaves, the rotating part of blocks, are made of bronze both for the jear knight-heads and for the topsail sheet bitts. Lignum-vitae (guaiacum), a self lubricating wood from the Caribbean, was traditionally used for the sheaves of running blocks and for the dead-eyes tensioning the shrouds.

The blocks were always made of elm but as the ravages of Dutch Elm disease have made this wood a rare commodity, the 900 blocks required of various types and sizes have been made out of ash, a very satisfactory substitute.

1. *Preparation in the forge of an iron strap to encase a swivelling block. Note the wooden blocks soaking in a pail of water* (photo AH SM).

2. *The blacksmith fits an iron strap around the swivelling block (see page 100)* (photo AH SM).

3. *A batch of ash or elm swivelling block shells fitted with their block straps and ready to receive their sheaves* (photo AH SM).

On the quarter-deck, the main-mast block-rack with its swivelling blocks in place and holes drilled for belaying pins. Just behind is the wooden grating acting as a skylight for the gun-deck below.

---

[5] Hearts and bull's-eyes, with spliced rope or iron straps around them and a single hole in the middle, allow a rope to run through an angle thus reducing the strain on it. Homer called them "wooden apples" and the Greeks and Egyptians used them. One of their uses is for tensioning the stays. Dead-eyes, which usually have three holes, are mainly used to tension the shrouds. Blocks with sheaves are more efficient and enable manoeuvres to be carried out with fewer men. Two blocks replace one man and three blocks replace two men.

1-2. *Luc Caquineau turning a cannon truck on the lathe with dead-eyes in the foreground. Middle photo : the same dead-eyes, now pierced with three eyes (holes) in the centre through which to lace the lanyards and with the "scores" hollowed out of the edges to take the wreathes of the straps or the iron bands of the shroud chains.* Photos AH.

3. *The dead-eyes with their iron straps will be used to tension the shrouds. They are used in pairs with one attached to the bottom of the shrouds and the other to the top link of the shroud chains. A lanyard is threaded alternately through the holes of the upper and lower dead-eyes giving a six-fold purchase (see page 95).*

The sails

The decision was taken to make up the frigate's sails using linen fabric woven in England. The fore-course is 231 m², the fore-top-sail 234 m² ; the main-course is 300 m², the main-top-sail 247 m² and the mizzen-sail 86 m². The total sail area is 900 to 1200 m². Initially, the sail wardrobe will consist fairly modestly of two sets of all the sails, but doing without special types of sail such as studding-sails for very fine weather and light winds.

Anne Renaud, a traditional sail maker, is making under the public eye the sails for the long-boat, the pinnace and the jolly-boat. (Photo AH).

Watched by the visitors, Anne Renaud is making the first sails for the frigate. Here she is finishing the smaller inner jib, which is nonetheless 50 m² (photo AH SM).

The capstans

To weigh the anchor and sway up the top-masts, ships are equipped with capstans, which are man-powered winches with a vertical axis. The main parts of a capstan are the drum and the spindle. The spindle heel is planted in a step on the deck below and rides on an iron saucer. The step and the partners, the frame in the higher deck, serve as bearings for the spindle (see page 100). The drum, with vertical ribs called whelps to give traction and increase the diameter without adding weight, is surmounted by a drum-head with square bar-holes cut in it to receive the levers.

The main capstan is sited on the gun-deck abaft the main-mast. Its twelve levers are cut from ash, one of the woods having the greatest flexibility and strength (also used for cart shafts).Each lever is pushed by two or three seamen and even five for the heaviest loads such as weighing the anchor (5 men on each of the 12 bars requires 60 men in all).

The voyol or messenger is a large rope in the form of a ring running from the hawse-holes to the capstan. To heave up the anchor, the cable, too thick and un-pliable to be wound round the capstan, is attached in several places to the voyol by special small ropes called nippers. When the operation is finished, the anchor cable is wound round the large cable bitt and its cross-piece (see page 100).

The fore or jear capstan , on the forecastle is used for working the rig.

1. *A carpenter works on the drum of the main capstan, made up of blocks of oak assembled in a ring around the centre spindle.* **2.** *The capstans are fitted with iron hoops to hold them together in the same way as the hubs of cart wheels. Here in the forge the last of the 4 hoops is being hot fitted. (photos AH SM).*

3. *The shipwright is conducting a trial fitting of one of the capstan levers. The six stanchions supporting the quarter-deck beams within the turning-circle of the capstan levers are hinged at the top and can be lifted out of the way when the capstan is being manned. The officers' stairway is visible in the background.*

On the main capstan, a close view of the 2 pawls, oak blocks just above the deck, one facing each way.

Fitting a heated hoop to the fore capstan. There are two hoops on the drum-head, one at the base of the drum or barrel and one around the spindle heel. (photos AH SM).

Only a century ago, a hundred sailors manning the main capstan of a sail and steam driven warship. (carte postale DR).

Manoeuvering the jear capstan into position on the forecastle. Its spindle will pass through the forecastle deck and be seated in the step on the gun-deck (see pages 89 & 100) Note the iron hoop round the spindle heel, which will turn on the iron saucer set into the step, a primitive bearing. (photo AH SM).

The long-boat, pinnace and jolly-boat

Ships of the line and frigates carried a long-boat, a pinnace and a jolly-boat. Those of the *Hermione*, with respective lengths of 10.5 m, 8.5 m and 6.5 m, have been reconstructed entirely out of oak, with 22 mm planks. The long-boat, with a beam of 2.5 m, weighs 2.7 tons and the smaller boats weigh respectively 1.5 and 0.8 tons. These ship's boats, for manoeuvres, towing and rescue, were stacked[6] on top of one another in the waist between the forecastle and the quarter-deck. They were lowered into the water by means of tackle fitted to the yard-arms.

A model of the Hermione *showing the waist with the stacked boats.*

ALEXANDRE GENOUD OF « BATEAUX BOIS »

In charge of a traditional shipyard, he is responsible for all work other than the construction of the frigate's hull.

Alexandre Genoud, on the left, during the building of the ship's boats.

---

[6] For this reason the benches can be taken out.

The pinnace and the jolly-boat in Rochefort harbour on the occasion of the launching of the pinnace in June 2007. They carry respectively 14 and 9 persons.

The long-boat, the largest of the ship's boats, carrying sail on its three masts. It can embark 16 seamen, a helmsman and several officers or distinguished passengers. (photo AH SM).

The dozen steps constituting the gangway or accommodation ladder are ready to be fixed to the side of the ship to enable people to embark from the long-boat by climbing to the deck. The steps are grooved to make them less slippery and have three semi-circular notches cut out of the rear edge to evacuate the water and to provide handholds. (photo AH SM).

Cross-pieces, two stout oak bars athwart the boat below the clamps (thick planks running longitudinally inside the boats sides, clearly seen in the photo below right). They enable the boats to be lifted with tackle from the yard-arms.

With the pinnace almost completed and fully planked, the cross-pieces are fitted. These square-sectioned oak timbers are shaped into round bars in the middle to avoid fraying the lifting ropes.

Here is the finished pinnace with the lifting cross-piece just forward of one of the two removable masts. There is a matching one in the stern. (jm /2, 2742).

Launching the jolly-boat on June 11th 2005 Photo AH.

The Thétis, *1819, lowers a boat into the water. N.M.N. Rochefort. M.N.M. Rochefort, photo JMB.*

Wash drawing by Pierre Ozanne, the Thames *lowering its boats, action of 25 Messidor, year IV (July 14th, 1796). Musée national de la Marine.*

The beauty and mystery of work in the forge. Vulcan, the god of fire and of metalworking, is not far away !
Fitting metal hoops to the fore capstan is in progress here. With the same technique as for cart wheels, a very
precisely dimensioned iron hoop, expanded by the heat of the forge, can be hammered into position, singeing
the wood somewhat. After cooling, it will shrink and exert very considerable pressure, squeezing tightly
together the assembled pieces of wood. photo AH SM.

The forge and the metal aboard

The forge

Watched by the visitors, the blacksmiths of the *Hermione* make the fixings of the stanchions (photo p 81), the capstan fittings, the deck beam knee brackets, the shroud chains, the guard-rail stanchions for the tops (photo p 96), the locks, the nails of the port-lids and all the fittings of the ship's boats.

FROM CRAFTSMANSHIP IN WROUGHT IRON TO THE SHIPYARD FORGE

A master blacksmith, Romain Botella, pictured below, and his two assistants work all the time under the gaze of the visitors to the shipyard. They have the dual tasks of making the parts for the *Hermione* as rapidly as possible to respect the contract, without risking incurring financial loss for the Métalnéo company, and being available to give explanations to the visitors.

Romain Botella manages to fulfil both requirements, because he loves his trade and likes communicating with the spectators. Everything is organized so that visitors will always see the forge in action, even on Sundays.

Romain Botella shaping the top stanchions with the power hammer. The forge will provide all the metal fittings for the frigate, such as knee brackets, gun carriage irons, shroud chains, iron ballast.

Previously engaged in making fine wrought iron, he has passed enthusiastically to naval forge work. Passionately interested by the *Hermione*, he has gathered information on the techniques used in the 18th century and on maritime history.

1. *A shroud chain on the left and hand-crow-levers used to manoeuvre the guns.*

2. *Bands fitting round the scores (edge grooves) of the dead-eyes.*

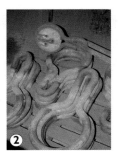

The anchors

The anchors, forged and finished in the forges at Guérigny, were installed under the control of the master anchor man in the ports of Rochefort and Brest. The sheet-anchor of the *Hermione*, found at the wreck site off Le Croisic, is 4.25 m high and weighs 1.5 tons.

The new main anchor will be custom made, but this does not exclude the use of a chain and modern anchor conforming to modern norms.

The anchor forge. Encyclopaedia of Diderot and Alembert.

Port of Toulon in 1756. Detail of the ordnance depot. Centre : lifting a gun onto its carriage with a heavy-load derrick. Behind : stacking of shot, shells and cannons (at rear) in the prescribed manner. In distance : ships laid up in reserve, with top-masts lowered. Foreground : carrying shells. Painting by Joseph Vernet, from a series on ports in France, ordered by Louis XV during the Seven Years War. Musée national de la Marine à Paris.

1. *Red hot 4 cm diameter iron bars being forged into bolt heads, shaped by the blacksmith by means of a concave headed maul (iron hammer)* (photo AH SM).

2. *Forged bolt head and eye of shroud chain into which it will be inserted.*

3. *Shroud chain bolts stacked on the gun-deck ready to be fitted, seen with the bottom links of the shroud chains lying on top of them.*

4. *A batch of shroud chain bolts which will be driven through the thickness of the ship's sides.*

Shroud chains

The lower ends of the shroud chains (see page 95) are fastened to the sides of the ship below the chain-wales, which are oak platforms projecting horizontally from the hull and serving to increase the distance of the bottom of the shrouds from the centre axis of the ship, thus giving a wider based support for the lower masts. The chains are held by huge bolts forged from iron bars 4 cm in diameter.

5. *Using a percussion press to pierce a hole in a red-hot bolt. A forelock will be threaded though the hole.* (photo AHSM).

6. *The lowest links of the shroud chains fastened at both ends by bolts passing though the thickness of the ship's sides below the chain-wales.* (photo AHSM).

The ordnance of the 18th century *Hermione*

Bronze and iron cannons

An old 8-pdr elm carriage found around 1800 in the Charente river near Rochefort.
Musée national de la Marine à Rochefort.

The ordnance (artillery) of a warship accounted for 20% of its overall cost ! This explains the major efforts to standardize from 1690 onwards, the concentration of cannon foundries and the replacement of bronze by iron, which was six times less expensive. By 1699, 85% of cannons were already made of iron[7].

The major foundries in the Dauphiné, Angoulême and Périgord regions cast the cannons and the small ones cast the shot. For the Rochefort dockyard, most of the ordnance came from the Ruelle foundry. The Rochefort foundry cast bronze cannons from 1669 until 1840, but never made any iron ones.

Cannons and calibres[8]

The 12-pdr guns carried by the *Hermione* were 2.65 m long and had a bore of 12 centimetres (12.126). The diameter of the 12 pound (5.4 kg) cannon balls was about 3.5 mm less than the bore of the gun. The difference between the diameters, known as the windage, avoided the risk of the gun exploding due to excessive momentary pressure. The length of a cannon is usually between 16 and 20 times the diameter of its bore. The *Hermione*'s guns, of the 1766 model, came from the decommissioning of the *Engageante*. 6-pdrs needed a gun crew of 6 men and 12-pdrs had 8 men and and a boy.

The shot embarked at the start of a cruise was 60 round-shot, 10 bar-shot and 10 canister-shot (small shot in a tin case) for each cannon, amounting to 12.74 tons for the 12-pdrs and 1.96 tons for the 6-pdrs.
In addition, there were 10 1-pdr swivel guns for the top platforms and the ship's boats, as well as muskets and pistols.

An authentic 12-pdr cannon mounted on a new carriage complete with breeching is presented on site.

---

[7] Taken from *L'Artillerie de mer de la marine française*, by Jean Boudriot. Iron is heavier and more dangerous if it explodes, but less noisy than bronze, which can be cast with ornate moulding.
[8] Data provided by Martine Acerra, Jean Boudriot and Jean Thomas.

The gun carriages

The order issued on January 9 1552 by Henri II obliged all populations to plant elms along the roads to provide wood for gun carriages. Elm, with knotted grain from repeated pollarding, does not split and does not shatter with flying splinters under the impact of grapeshot, thus limiting the wounding of sailors and gun crews. But Dutch elm disease has decimated the population of elms in recent decades.

The carriages were part of the ship, but the cannons belonged to the stock of ordnance. In order to avoid killing the gun crews, the recoil of the cannon was limited by strong ropes called breeching attached to ringbolts in the ship's sides. After re-loading, the gun was run out of the ports again by two gun-tackles, one on each side of the carriage. Train-tackle, hooked to an eye-bolt in the train (after part of the gun carriage) and to a ring-bolt in the deck, enabled the crew to run in the gun, notably to load it when the ship was heeled to the lee side.

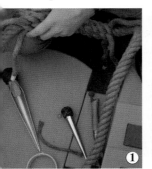  

1. *In the Corderie Royale de Rochefort, splicing ropes for the train-tackle. (photo AH).* **2.** *With its quoin, a wedge under the cannon breech to regulate the height of fire, one of the gun carriages, numbered as in the 18th century, with even numbers for the starboard battery and odd numbers for the port battery.* **3.** *Set of quoins.*

The *Hermione's* guns	Calibre	Weight in tons Cannon + carriage	Number	Weight in tons guns + shot = total
Upper decks	6	0.84 +0.2 = 1.04	8	8.32 +1.96 = 10.28
Gun deck	12	1.6 +0.3 = 1.90	26	49.4 + 12.74 = 62.14
Total				57.72 + 14.7 = 72.42
So the *Hermione's* guns weighed 58 tons and she carried nearly 15 tons of shot.				

1. *Different stages in the production of gun carriage trucks, un-shaped blocks, right, to painted red ready to be mounted, left. There are 128 of them, made of ash instead of the traditional elm.* **2.** *Display of the various iron parts on a carriage, forged on the spot.*

3. *Carriage being constructed : note the iron reinforcing bar across the middle. Photo AH.*
4. *A set of carriages in their final stages. Photo AH.*

5. *A part of the Hermione's handsome set of gun carriages and a few barrels – for gunpowder, drink and salted meat – also ready.* **6.** *Finished gun carriages with their breeching ropes and one fitted with a copy of a 12 pdr cannon.*

Accessories : hand-crow-levers, sponges, worms and ladles

With their cannon mounted, the gun carriages were very heavy and had to be moved and aimed with a pair of hand-crow-levers, a particular form of hand-spike. These long levers with claws at the bottom were initially made of metal (see page 111) but these damaged the decks and were replaced with levers made of ash, elm or oak.

7. *Copper gunpowder ladles for loading the guns. (photo AH SM).* **8.** *Oak sponges, for ramming home the charge and cleaning out the guns after each explosion, await their coverings of leather (photo AH SM).* **9.** *Worms, with heads like double cork-screws, to draw out the residue of the charge after at least every third discharge. (photo AH SM).*

Port of Toulon, 1756, detail of the naval ordnance depot. Reamers are boring or trueing up a cannon. Painting by Joseph Vernet. Musée national de la Marine.

One of the Hermione's *gun carriages with a hand-spike to move and aim the gun.*

How the cannons are cast

Around a wooden model of the cannon a hollow mould in two halves was made from clay mixed with horse dung to make it refractory. The mould was stood up vertically and the molten metal poured into it. The bore was subsequently hollowed out.

The cannons of the new *Hermione* will either be made of iron, but with thinner walls than the originals, or else will be cast in aluminium and painted black, as has been done for other replicas. In either case, they will not be fit to fire real shot, but will be able to fire blank salutes during maritime festivals.

Shot-racks containing 10 balls of 12 pounds or 15 balls of 6 pounds.

Alexandre Genoud checking a new copy against an original rack.

Around the main-mast, the four well-pump cylinders, to be fitted into the semi-circular cut-outs, limit the footprint of the shot-locker in the hold.

Shot locker and shot racks

The shot ready for use was kept in triangular wooden racks near each gun. The reserve supply was kept in the shot locker at the bottom of the hold, immediately forward of the main-mast step. Its rectangular base, about 1 m by 1.3 m, was determined by the spacing of the four well pumps and it extended vertically from the top of the keelson up to the orlop deck. To load it or take shot out of it, a gunner went down and used a strong canvas bag slung from a hoist. As it was vital not to make a mistake in the heat of battle, partitions separated the 6 pound and 12 pound shot.

Gunpowder

A frigate carried 2.5 tons of powder[9], a precise mixture of sulphur, nitre, and wood charcoal of alder buckthorn or black alder, small forest shrubs greatly in demand for this purpose.

The effects of gunfire

A broadside is the simultaneous discharge of all the guns on one side of a ship. Round-shot could be fired into the enemy's hull, with the aim of damaging the ship and killing the gun crews, or bar-shot could be fired into the rigging to bring down the masts. It is commonly held that the French fired high to destroy, sails, rigging and masts, while the British concentrated their fire on the hulls to sink the enemy ship, but all sorts of differing views have been expressed and the object was often to take the captured ship back home as a prize. The British Admiralty repaired and put back into service a large number of French ships, considered to be admirably designed.

The round-shot sent showers of mortally dangerous wood splinters flying across the deck, but the wood of the sides often seemed to close up. To prevent water infiltration, the ship's carpenters hammered in ready-made pieces of hardwood, called shot-plugs, of different sizes according to the calibre of shot causing the damage.

---

[9] Calculation by Jean Thomas, based on information provided by Jean Boudriot.

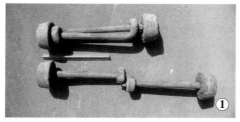

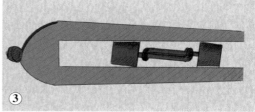

1. *Unusual types of expanding bar-shot, made near Nantes under Napoleon Bonaparte : from a cargo retrieved from the river Erdre.*

2. *Conventional double-headed or bar-shot. Chain-shot, with the halves linked by chain, was also used.*

3. *The expanding bar-shot had sawn-off cone shaped ends to give a flusher fit in the gun barrel.*

The gun-ports of a ship

Gun-ports and guns

Gun-ports[10] are openings in the ship's sides, allowing gun muzzles to be run out of them. The ports were cut out when the hull was almost finished and this required the sawing of some of the ribs. It was only with the more precise and sophisticated ship designs produced early in the 19th century that the gun-ports were incorporated in the original concept and ways were found to avoid cutting the pieces of crooked wood, which were so rare and hard to find.

So that the structure of the ship would not be unduly weakened and to avoid the lower gun-deck crews from being hampered by the flame flashes of the guns on the deck above, the ports were staggered laterally and were never directly above one another. The spacing of the guns, about 1.7 m apart, was enough to ensure that gun-crews did not get in each other's way.

1. *Finishing a gun-port on the quarter-deck rails for 6 pdr guns. Note that the upper-works planks are of fir or pine to lessen the weight carried high up. The lower planks are always oak. (Photo AH SM).*

2. *A view of the whole gun-deck after it had been caulked. The excess pitch still has to be removed from the seams. The gun-ports are ready to take their 12 pdr guns (Photo AH SM).*

---

[10] Invented around 1500 by the master shipwright at Brest, Descharges, and first used on the *Charente*.

Port lids

The gun-ports could be closed by port-lids to prevent water from entering the gun-deck in a turbulent sea. They pivoted on overhead hinges, so as not to be torn off. During engagements they were opened and secured parallel to the surface of the water, before the guns were run out. In rough seas and if the ship was heeling, the ports of the lower gun-deck on the leeward side had to be closed, or else enough water might be shipped to sink the vessel. Under such conditions, a captain who managed to place himself to the lee of his adversary and thus remain able to use his lower battery, obtained a decisive advantage. Frigates did not usually have real port-lids.

Bow chaser gun-ports and stern raft-ports

On the *Hermione*, as on all frigates of the same type, the only ports to be fitted with hinged lids were those of the two bow chasers on the gun-deck and the loading ports, called raft-ports, on the orlop-deck immediately under the ship's counter.

Half port-lids

The stern chaser ports of frigates often had half-ports, with upper and lower hinged halves. When the sea was rough, the lower halves could be closed while the guns remained run out.

False port-lids

Proper port-lids were often reserved for the lower gun-deck of ships of the line and false port-lids used for the upper gun-decks or those of smaller warships such as frigates and corvettes. According to the naval dictionary of Admiral Willaumez (1763-1845) "it is a square of planks fitting into rabbets round the gun-port. The muzzle of the gun emerges through a hole cut in the middle and a screen of painted canvas fitting closely round the cannon keeps the sea out."

Port-lids of HMS Victory, *Nelson's flagship dating from the same period as the* Hermione *and open to visitors at Portsmouth.*

Half port-lids of a frigate : the lower half is closed here to keep out spray when the ship is under way. Musée national de la Marine à Brest, photo JMB.

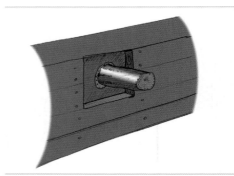

Sketch of a planked false port-lid with oil-cloth screen. The Hermione *was probably fitted with an arrangement of this sort, enabling her to keep her guns permanently run out ready to fire.*

The two bow chaser gun-ports for firing at a ship being pursued are cut in the ship's sides near to the cheeks of the head (see pages 86 & 87). They are fitted with hinged port-lids to avoid shipping water from large waves. The port side gun-port-lid, closed here (it can be seen open on page 134), forward of a port without a lid (the latter will get a false lid).

Fitting the lids to the raft-ports in the counter, one on either side of the helm-port, the hole through which the rudder head passes. (see page 130) (photo AH SM).

View of the gun-room, used by the master gunner, at the aft end of the orlop deck, now finished and beneath the ward-room on the gun-deck (see also pages 129, 130 & 131). The two raft-ports in the counter serve to load long items such as spare masts and spars.

Life on board, from decorum to hard labour
The modest decoration of a frigate, carvings, gilding

Carved figures on ships

Gilded baroque carvings came to cover the prow and the entire stern of warships during the reign of Louis XIV. Around 1760, the discontinuation of poop decks lowered the taffrail, which adopted the simplified horse-shoe shape to be seen on the Hermione. The large carvings disappeared and the neo-classical ornamentation became more discreet. The quarter-galleries replaced the substantial lateral overhangs of the former after-castles.

The desire for grandeur of Napoleon's Empire brought a return of the heavy ornamentation.

The figurehead of the Massiac, *one of the last French East Indiamen, launched 1759, with a lion rampant, holding between its fore-paws the shield of France with three fleurs de lys, was similar to that of the* Hermione. *Model in the Musée de la Marine, photo Boudriot.*

The decoration of the *Hermione*

Figureheads were intended to impress the adversary and show the glory of the monarch. Previously many different figures were represented, but under Louis XIV a lion became the standardized form and this design was used for the *Hermione* and her sister-ship the *Concorde*.

The carvings on the counter have been re-created by copying from period models.

The horseshoe shaped taffrails are typical of their period. The decoration, both of the pediments of buildings and of the sterns of frigates, was restrained and perfectly convergent in Louis XVI's Navy. They featured the shield of France, surrounded by flags, anchors, cannons and shot.

Left : the frigate, the Dédaigneuse *in the Musée national de la Marine at Rochefort. Right : 1/36th scale model of the* Hermione *by Jean-Claude Cossais.*

The carving of the taffrail was begun in the summer of 2009 and that of the figurehead, a lion, in 2010 (described on pages 86, 87 and 122).

1. *The horseshoe shaped taffrail, seen in July 2009, has yet to receive its decorative carvings. The windows of the ward-room are separated by 7 elegant pilasters.*

2. *A German carver, Jens-Ole Remmers, carves a frieze onto the "horseshoe"* (photo AH SM).

3. *The frieze is embellished with blue and yellow paint* (photo AH SM).

4. *Carving the lambrequin, carved drapery or fronds surrounding the shield of France.* (photo AH SM).

5. *The royal arms with three fleurs de lys carved from the oak.* (photo AH SM).

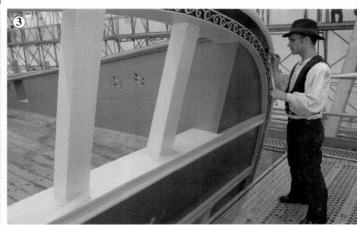

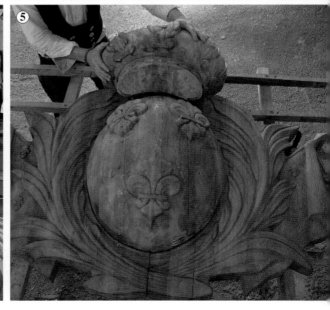

1. *The King's arms coated with primer paint, before being put in position on the taffrail.*

2. *Detail of the carved shell at both ends of the* Hermione *name board.* (photo AH SM).

Les dorures

1. *Gilding the fleurs de lys and the crown after fitting the arms to the taffrail and plugging the holes.* (photo AH SM).

2. *Applying gold leaf to the crown, the fleurs de lys of the shield and the inner part of the green lambrequin. Bénédicte Rousselot used 250 sheets of pure gold one micron thick.* (photo AH SM).

Shipboard life, interior arrangements and fittings

The internal layout and arrangements are described in the texts accompanying the cutaway drawings on pages 88 to 90.

The officers' living quarters

All warships had a great cabin, known as the ward-room, in the stern. The commander of the port of Rochefort received a secret message from the Minister for the Navy, Mr de Sartine, signed at Versailles on February 29th 1780, containing a precise order. "The Marquess of La Fayette has papers and other personal effects and consequently it is necessary that he should have aboard a lodging that is closed and decent. The intention of the King is that on the frigate this staff officer should feel as safe and comfortable as possible."[11] The carpenters immediately set about installing these quarters with removable partitions, which were certainly subsequently removed when the elected representatives of Massachusetts were received aboard the *Hermione* in Boston harbour and for the special reception for the American Congress on May 4th 1781 for the official announcement of the victory in the naval battle of Chesapeake on March 16 .
The officers had small cabins on the orlop deck beneath the captain's cabin.
The furnishings and inside panelling were embellished with Louis XV style mouldings. The more rectilinear Louis XVI style was only just developing and the dockyard cabinet makers did not yet have the necessary tooling.

At the aft end of the gun-deck, the great cabin is lit by large stern gallery windows from which stern chaser guns could be fired. The boards placed on the deck indicate the positions of the removable partitions enclosing the berths.
1. On the starboard side La Fayette's cabin was lit by a glazed-in gun-port. **2.** On the port side, the cabin of La Fayette's second-in-command has already been erected. **3.** In the middle between the two, the ward-room lit by the stern windows had a large chart table which was also used for meals. There is direct access to the two quarter-galleries (conveniences). **4 & 5.** The 4 rectangles show the cabins and beds of the captain and his first lieutenant. **6 & 7.** On either side of the captain's cabin, were the aftermost 12 pdr guns of the broadside. They could be dragged aft to act as stern-chasers firing through the stern gallery windows.

---

[11] Letter from the naval archives in the port of Rochefort, quoted in "L'Hermione" by Kalbach and Gireaud, published by Editions Dervy.

Cabins of La Fayette and of the captain of the Hermione :

The great cabin, occupying the space between the stern counter and the officers' stairway, was divided up during sea voyages by removable partitions with Louis XV style mouldings and carvings. For the comfort of the captain and his guests, the cabin had handsomely finished oak foot-waling (inner planking lining the hull), a false ceiling and a good quality parquet.

1. Along the ship's side, the berth of the cabin of La Fayette's second-in-command.

2. In the middle, the two cabins of the captain and his first-lieutenant, lit by a window. (photo AH SM).

3. *Putting in the ceilings, flooring and partitions. The foot-waling is painted. (Photo AH SM).*

4. *The finished counter, the lower row of openings being the stern gallery lighting the great cabin. (Photo AH SM).*

The officers' quarters and stairway

All three levels of the stern section of the ship were for the exclusive use of the officers. Situated just forward of the mizzen-mast, the officers' stairs ran down from the quarter-deck to the gun-deck, where were the ward-room and the cabins of La Fayette, the captain and their lieutenants. It continued down to the orlop deck where there were the berths of the other officers and the cabins of the chaplain and the master gunner (see the later section on the rudder).

1. *1/36th scale model of the* Hermione *by Jean-Claude Cossais: details of the mizzen mast and of the officers' stairway. Note the beauty of the starboard quarter-gallery, despite its humble function of housing the officers' conveniences, and the aftermost gun-port with no gun and glazed window-pane grid. This was the window of La Layette's cabin.*

2. The officers' stairway installed. View from the gun-deck, looking down to the orlop deck.

View of the quarter-deck. Going aft successively, the rack of swivelling blocks for the main-mast running rigging, the grating lighting the main capstan, the officers' bench, the companion protecting the officers' stairs and the double row of hen coops. In the hull below can be seen the gun-port openings of the gun-deck.

The crew

The crewmen had sparse living conditions. Their hammocks were slung from the deck-beams between the guns on ships with more than one gun-deck. When clearing for action, the order "Up all hammocks" was given and they were rolled up, with the clothes inside and tied in the nettings inside the bulwarks to form a barricade against splinters and small shot. After the engagement, they were once again slung below the deck. On frigates, the hammocks were slung in the orlop deck (see pages 88 to 90). The height below the deck-beams in the Hermione was 1.54 m and that below the deck planks between the beams 1.75 m, so it was better not to be too tall ! By contrast, on the gun-deck and in the great cabin, there was 2.05 m below the beams and 2.15 m below the planking.

Accommodation of the junior officers

The warrant officers and petty officers, the master-caulker, carpenter, boatswain, etc. had the benefit of small berths in the bows on the port and starboard sides of the orlop deck (see pages 88 to 90).

1. *The coops for the hens which provided eggs and fresh meat for the ward-room table. The wounded and those suffering from scurvy were entitled to boiled chicken. The hens are in a safe place aft of the officers' bench and companionway.*

2. *The galley panel on the forecastle just aft of the fore-mast and the jear capstan. Its copper chimneys could be swivelled to whatever direction required. The panel forms a watertight basin to retain water to cool the chimneys as a precaution against fire. Note the two pivoting wooden pawls forward of the capstan foot. (photo AH SM).*

Cooking and food

Food for the crew of warships was very basic. It was prepared in the galley situated on the gun-deck just aft of the spindle of the jear capstan. The staple diet consisted of biscuit, beans and a soup made out of leftovers, bread crusts and biscuits, "the seaman's black gruel". Little meat was served, never more than once per day, and it was very rarely fresh (salted meat and fish were stored in wooden casks).

The regulation ration was five sheep per hundred men for every month at sea (with a few pigs in addition). For six months and for the three hundred men aboard the Hermione, 90 sheep were shipped. The sheep pen was situated on the orlop deck beneath the ships' boats (see p.89).

Meals were served "per dish", a group of seven men sharing a piece of meat handed out in the morning, strung on a skewer with their identifying marking. On days of fast, such as Fridays, meat was replaced by cheese, which was not much liked. Water was even more precious than wine, both being kept in wooden casks.

The rudder, the tiller and the wheel

The back or inner part of the rudder, which is linked to the stern-post, transmits the rotational force applied by the tiller. The main-piece of the rudder, sometimes extended by the after-piece if greater breadth is required, is the blade which acts on the water. Its width increases from top to bottom. At the widest part, it is one twelfth of the length of the midship deck-beam. "Rudder-irons", in fact made of bronze, hold the rudder to the stern-post. Braces or goodgeons, with large holes on the after part, are bolted round the stern-post. Bolted to the back of the rudder and also serving as reinforcing plates, the other parts of the hinges, called pintles, have strong cylindrical pins which fit into the eyes of the braces. The back of the rudder is made of a straight-grained piece of oak, without twisted fibres so as to withstand the torsion. Its leading edge is rounded to turn around the stern-post. The rudder-head passes into the counter through the helm-port, where rudder-coats of tarred canvas prevent water from coming in.

The rudder is attached to the hull by two chains so as not to lose it if grounding or a gale forced it off its hinges. A spare rudder is also carried aboard.

Just beneath the gun-deck, the foremost end of the tiller glides on a semi-circular plank called the sweep, fixed to the deck-beams. The tiller-rope runs from the fore end of the tiller, via a tackle system, vertically up to the quarter-deck where it is wound round the barrel of the ship's wheel. It is possible to install an emergency tiller in the great cabin.

In the free space left beyond the arc of movement of the tiller, there are two cabins, the chaplain's to starboard and the master-gunner's to port. Trustworthy men were needed in the area which, behind the partition for the captain's provisions, gave access to the powder room, placed below the biscuit store. There is another, smaller, powder room in the fore hold.

Details of the model of the Hermione *: the rudder and the rudder-irons.*

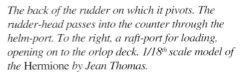

The back of the rudder on which it pivots. The rudder-head passes into the counter through the helm-port. To the right, a raft-port for loading, opening on to the orlop deck. 1/18th scale model of the Hermione *by Jean Thomas.*

Brace and pintle (seen turned 90° to starboard) of the Golymin, *a 74-gun ship wrecked off Brest in 1814. They are identical to the irons seen on the photos on the left.*

Stern of the real ship.

Inside of the model : the rudder-head passes through the counter. The tiller, beneath the beams of the gun-deck, goes forward to the tiller-sweep. Above the gun-deck (planking not yet installed), the top of the rudder-head has a mortise to take the emergency tiller operated in the great cabin. Photo Jean Thomas.

1/18th scale model of the Hermione ; details of the tiller-sweep on the orlop deck, with the chaplain's cabin right background, above the powder room.
Photo de Jean Thomas.

On the orlop deck aft. : arc of movement of the tiller, port side. The shipwright is in the space where the master-gunner's cabin was situated, opposite that of the chaplain.

A spiral grained oak like this one could not be used for the rudder. Its fibres would be cut when being squared off.

The double wheel with the drum for the tiller rope.

The *Hermione*'s hold

There were numerous store-rooms, such as that for dry vegetables, beans and peas, vital food for seamen (see section drawings pages 88 and 90).

A frigate carried in its hold many barrels of food, water, wine, gun-powder, etc. There were also the powder room, the shot locker and all necessary equipment, tools and spares. The *Hermione* was supposed to stow bales containing 4 000 uniforms for the rebel militias, but the delivery arrived after the ship had left.

The reconstructed *Hermione* will have different arrangements, with some removable fixtures, depending on whether she is at sea or berthed at Rochefort.

It is necessary to produce an 18th century ship open to visitors at Rochefort, which can also go to sea from time to time. It has been decided to install in the hold removable facilities and fittings such as showers, kitchens, engines, tanks and all the ducts and electrical wiring.

On the fore part of the orlop deck, beyond the double door a sliding door hides the dry vegetable store-room. Photo Jean Thomas.

The hold, seen here as it was in July 2009, will be partitioned off according to requirements.

The bilge-pumps in the bottom of the hold. At their bases can be seen metal pipes with strainers at the end placed in the space between two floor-timbers. (photo AH SM).

The hold and the bilge pumps

A large number of ships have foundered because the pumps could not evacuate water fast enough to cope with leaks and seepage. In spite of the quality of the caulking, long sea voyages would loosen the jaunts in the timbers and cause movement in the hull, thus deteriorating the water-tightness of the seams between the planks. The water pumps are vital pieces of equipment aboard wooden vessels and great care was always taken with their construction and their maintenance by the ship's carpenters.

The four pump bodies (positions shown on page 94) surround the heel of the main-mast, as it is the lowest point inside the hull, the place where bilge-water gathers. They were traditionally made of elm, a wood that can withstand being constantly wet, as is the case with bilge-pumps.

The pumps were worked by men on the quarter-deck using wooden levers called brakes.

1. *Carpenters assembling the pump casings traditionally made of elm.* (photo AH SM).

2. *In the forge, heated metal bands being fitted round the pump casings.* (photo AH SM).

3. *The 2 "brakes", pump handles worked on the quarter-deck.*

4. *The 4 pumps in position around the main-mast (not yet fitted) with the large main-mast knight-head behind them. Four cannon balls, encircled by leather thongs, serve as counter weights to take the piston of each pump down again after its upward stroke by means of the brakes. The canvas pump-hose, fitted to the water outlet of the nearest pump, is seen folded up. In service, it would be run out to the scuppers, channels draining the water from the deck into the sea (see page 84).*

5. *Trial of the pumps with the brake, using a post to replace the main-mast. The seamen are hauling on the splayed ropes. The pumps proved to have a very efficient rate of discharge with the pump-hose extended.* (photo AH SM).

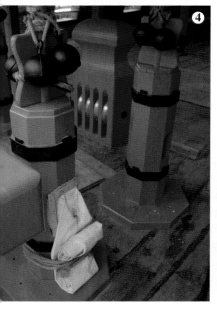

The final operations of the shipwrights

Finishing the hull : fitting the cut-water

1. *Fitting the cut-water in the presence of the public 10 June 2007. To avoid any distortion during fitting, the assembly is held in a frame.* **2.** *In July 2009, the lion figurehead has not yet been fitted to the cut-water (see pages 86, 87 and 122). Note the open port-hole for the bow-chaser gun.* **3.** *Fitting the kevel-heads, top timbers rising above the gun-wales and the forecastle bulwarks, serving to belay ropes (photo AH SM).* **4.** *The hull planking almost finished, with only a single strake of planks still to be laid. Compare this with the openwork with only alternate strakes shown on page 75. This operation is comparable to laying contiguous planking, but even more difficult. The longest planks of 74 mm thick oak are over 10 m long and weigh 200 kg. Their shape is drawn and they are cut out using a temp-plate replicating the curve of the hull.*

Fitting the kevel-heads

These are sturdy top timbers mounted above some of the hawse-pieces and protruding above the bulwarks around the forecastle (see page 136). With their shaped necks and heads, they are used to tie up large ropes, sheets, hawsers and the shank-painter for securing the anchor shank.

Laying the last hull planks

Owing to the considerable length of time taken to build the ship, the planking was initially applied as openwork with alternate strakes to allow the wood to dry out. In places the drying has been excessive. To complete the hull planking, the remaining planks are cut out to very precisely measured shapes before being forced into place. The seams are then caulked. For this operation, nine highly specialized shipwrights were brought from the Bernard boatyard at Saint Vaast la Hougue on the coast of Normandy, to reinforce the existing team. This brought the strength of the workforce up to thirty, each person exercising his special skills under the gaze of the visiting public.

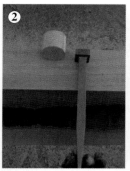

1. *Fastening on the closing planking with large bronze nails. (photo AH SM).* **2.** *A 74 mm thick hull plank shown with a bronze nail and the plug which will cover the hole over the head (see further on).* **3.** *The plugs of different sizes are cut out of an oak plank with a hole saw respecting the direction of the wood fibres. Plugs sliced from a cylindrical pole would all have porous end-grain on their outer faces.*

...ame section of hull after all the closing ...s had been laid. During the summer of ... the shipwrights, using a flexible strip ...od as a guide, planed down the hull to ...e perfectly smooth lines. The surface ...i ready for painting.

...rting furrs of different shapes, ...e seen here being long, slim fillets. ...y are glued with resorcinol to the ...ks of the ship's bottom. Above ...i can be seen nail-head plugs, ...rted and planed flush, and holes ...et unplugged.

Various finishing operations, furrs and plugs

Furrs or furrens : To avoid any risk of leaks but also for technical or aesthetic reasons, certain defective sections of wood are removed and replaced by a "furr", a fillet of wood of the same species (oak) of precisely the same shape and respecting the direction of the grain. Because of the size of the frigate and the number of furrs required, the shipwright cut out a set of temp-plates so as to be able to use a plunge router to remove the defective wood rapidly and accurately.

Plugs : Pieces of wood assembled with bolts, nails or metal pins are finished off with a small wooden cylindrical plug to seal and protect the metal fastening. The plug is glued and forced into the hole respecting the direction of grain of the surrounding wood, before being planed flush.

Painting

The paint used was a mixture of linseed oil and siccative.

After the history committee had conducted extensive research to determine the colours of the 18th century *Hermione*, the original pigments were found and re-used. Red, to hide the blood, according to popular rumour, for all of the gun-deck, the quarter-deck and forecastle[12]. For the bulwarks, the blue of the Kings of France, a costly colour as it contained ground lapis lazuli. Naples yellow[13], was often used to produce the effect of gold at the level of the gun-ports and a recipe of 1680 has been successfully re-used. The remaining part of the ship's sides was painted black, while the bottom underwater was off-white, using a mixture of tallow pitch and pine rosin. The first layers of paint were applied in June 2009 on the bulwarks (see photo on the following page).

[12] Red pigment comes from red ochre and the yellow from natural clay containing ferrous oxide, so these colours were inexpensive. The Dutch, who were not colour-blind, painted their gun-decks green.
[13] See the yellow paint (now faded to off-white) of HMS Victory on page 120.

Painting is underway. The bulwarks have already been painted blue, the colour of the King of France, and yellow. The non-authentic safety rails on metal uprights inboard from the bulwarks of the forecastle and the kevel-heads show the scale of the Hermione, *which is a large vessel. (Photo AH SM)*

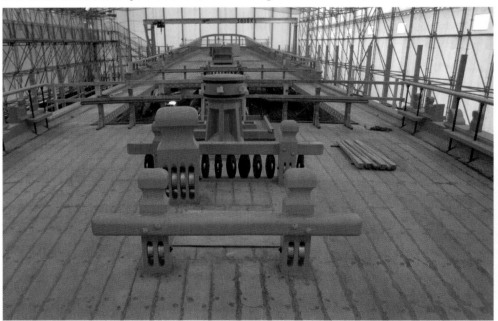

View of the entire upper deck, forecastle and quarter-deck, 44 m in overall length. Just behind the foremost rack, a safety panel hides the partners of the fore-mast. Going aft, there are then the large fore-mast knight-head, the swivelling block rack and the jear capstan with its levers on the deck on the right. The amidships waist will receive the ship's boats and the quarter-deck is at the far end. (photo AH SM).

Chapter VII
The association and the future for the l'*Hermione*

Who is reconstructing the *Hermione* ?

Why this reconstruction project ?

In the early 1990s, a handful of people who felt nostalgia for the long gone navy of sailing ships, of admirers of the buildings of the Rochefort dockyards willed by Louis XIV, of its unique dry docks and its rope making factory, and of enthusiasts for sea-going life, all of them confronted by the loss of activity of the town of Rochefort, starting with the closing of the dockyard in 1927 and worsened by the subsequent departure of the Navy, sought a federative solution. An idea began to be discussed by a group of enthusiasts connected with the Centre International de la Mer and with the municipality of Rochefort. Why not give new life to the dockyard which had provided Rochefort with a livelihood ? Why not reconstruct the most famous of the 550 ships built in the dockyard ? So the choice fell on the *Hermione*, the ship associated with La Fayette. The *Hermione* became the focal centre of a major overall project for the town of Rochefort, with a new exploitation of the cultural heritage represented by the dockyard and rope factory. Since June 15th, 2009, this project has been placed under the high patronage of the President of the Republic of France.

The actors and the sponsors of the project

For the historical monuments, the leading lights were Jean-Louis Frot, former mayor and Bruno Coussy, municipal architect. The naval history aspect was the responsibility of Emmanuel de Fontainieu, director of the Centre International de la Mer housed in the royal rope factory. For the *Hermione*, the project coordinators were Erik Orsenna, founder-president of the association Hermione-La Fayette, and Benedict Donnelly, son of an American who had taken part in the D-Day landings in Normandy, who took over the presidency in 1994.

Nothing would have been possible without the commitment and the determination of several regional bodies, including the Rochefort municipality and the public authorities of the Charente-Maritime Département and the Poitou-Charentes Region. The European Union contributed some funds. Many companies in the Poitou-Charentes region became members of the "*Hermione* Circle of regional enterprises" and those throughout the rest of France adhered to the "Companions of the *Hermione*".

The association founder-president, Erik Orsenna, (left) sitting on a floor timber in the early stages of the construction in April 1999 with Georges Pernoud, presenter of the television programme Thalassa, the magazine of the sea. Photo AH.

The association Hermione - La Fayette

The association has 4 000 members and 24 Board Members, including the representatives of public bodies and of the founder members, and three representatives of the contributing associates.

The U.S.A. is already very interested in the inaugural voyage and in the commemoration of everything connected with the War of Independence and the role of La Fayette.

It is for this reason that there is an American foundation for the *Hermione*, presided over by two former American ambassadors to France, and an association "Hermione

in America", presided over by a former French ambassador to Washington, to promote the inaugural voyage.

The estimated cost of reconstructing such a vessel is 17 million euros, a substantial sum that is nevertheless only a tenth of the budget needed for building an America's Cup contender.

Colonel Pierre Gras, one of the most devoted board members, with a model of the Hermione.

MARYSE VITAL

The secretary-general of the association, certainly one of its mainstays and somewhat its moving spirit, does not hesitate to say that "the closer we get to the status of a floating monument, the more complicated the problems become". A huge amount of work is involved in coordinating all the participants, finding the funding for the construction work, handling the daily affairs of the association and integrating all of this in a large project with an unusually long lifespan.

Maryse Vital and F. Asselin.

It is constantly necessary to deal with pressing problems at the same time as doing long term planning.

So much energy and application is required that some people might be tempted to say that the *Hermione* is more like a slave galley than a frigate !

(L) Isabelle Georget, Communications manager. (R) Jean Thomas and Stéphane Munari, communications.

Who is reconstructing the *Hermione* ?

There are unpaid volunteers in the association, but the reconstruction of a vessel the size of the *Hermione* requires professionals, as much for reasons of safety as for efficiency. The pilot and the director of the project are J-F. Fountaine and L. Darold.

Contractors have been selected after public tender procedures :
- the wooden hull, which represents the bulk of the work, has been entrusted to the Asselin and Bernard companies,
- the forging of the various metal fittings has been attributed to the Métalnéo company,
- the Bateau Bois company of Alexandre Genoux is making the gun carriages, the mast tops (platforms) and the three ship's boats,
- a wood turner, Luc Caquineau, is producing the belaying pins, dead-eyes and gun-carriage trucks. Another turner is responsible for the masts and spars,
- a sail-making craftswoman, Anne Renaud, is cutting out and making up in the traditional way the sails for the ship's boats, while an industrial sail maker is producing those of the frigate,
- the ropes are being supplied by a specialist, some in natural hemp others in synthetic fibres. Demonstrations for the visitors concerning rope making, particularly the gun-breeching, are planned,
- rigging specialists will install the masts, spars and all the fittings of the rig.

In all, a dozen different trades are called upon, woodcutters, shipwrights, caulkers, carpenters, wood-carvers, blacksmiths, riggers, sail-makers, painters, etc., not forgetting the historian, the naval architect and the draughtsman.

In the high season, 60 people are employed on the *Hermione* project :
- 30 shipwrights and blacksmiths building the ship,
- 30 people, including 10 in the Centre International de la Mer, for managing and guiding the visitors.

During the monthly site meetings involving the naval architect, the consultant shipwright, the contracting companies, the secretary-general and other members of the association, all the participants discuss current problems. It is constantly necessary to re-invent forgotten techniques and skills and find again old savoir-faire. How to find the design of the stern-frame and then shape the timber, how to mount the mast top platforms and make the stanchions for the guard rails, is it necessary to put iron hoops on the lower masts ? All the participants have had to ask questions time and time again and come up with answers by collective thinking, backed up by history.

December 1996 : signature of the contract for the first phase of work by the president Benedict Donnelly (left) and the contractor, François Asselin (centre), in the presence of Jean-Louis Frot, mayor of Rochefort at that time. Photo AH.

The vice-president, Alain Bourdeaux and the treasurer, Olivier Pagézy were also involved.

The stages of the construction, the progress of the project

1988 to 1990 : emergence of the project, issue by the town of Rochefort of "memory of La Fayette and of the *Hermione*" medal.

1992, end of year : creation of the association.

1993, September : for national heritage day, setting up of the full scale metal skeleton of the Hermione's hull in the double dry dock. Thought up and made by Raymond Labbé, it gave a precise idea of the size and bulk of the ship.

1996 : choice of the Asselin company. At that time the aim was to launch the boat in 2007 and so in 1997 the logo "Hermione 2007"was produced.

1997, February : production of templates by the drawing office and search for first timbers.

1997, 4th of July : symbolically on the American Independence Day holiday, laying of the keel, the act marking the birth of a ship.

1197 to 1999 : production and installation of 62 ribs, fitting of the stem, late 1999.

2000 and 2001 : making of deck beams, knees and work inside hull.

2002 : start of the fitting of outside planking, the skin of the vessel.

2003 : start of the making of the stern frame and fitting of the taffrail.

Each stage of the construction provides an opportunity to organize a public event in front of the tent structure housing the Hermione. *The Charente river is seen in the background.* AH, photo Françis Latreille.

2004 : installation of foot-waling in the hold, of the six pillars supporting the orlop deck and its binding strakes and carlings.

2005 : installation of the gun deck with supporting pillars, the riders in the hold, finishing the taffrail, making of the jolly boat.

2006 : installation of quarter-deck and forecastle with gratings, making of the tops.

2007 : construction of the head, forward of the stem, with the cut-water and standard knee, much work inside hull at level of orlop and gun decks. Fore-top-gallant yard made.

2008 : finishing and painting the bulwarks, finishing the decks with caulking and sealing with pitch. Making of some of the masts and yards.

2009 : completing the foot-waling, fitting of last hull strakes to close off planking, until then left in openwork, caulking. In Great Cabin, fitting of parquet, ceiling and partitions for cabins of La Fayette and ship's captain. Carving, painting and gilding of the taffrail. Installing capstans and pumps.

2010 : fitting of the cheeks of the head (see pages 86, 87), chain-wales, steps for the mast heels. Carving and fitting of figurehead. Completion of masts, yards, rigging and sails. Start construction of quarter-galleries.

2011 : completion of quarter-galleries, rigging, caulking, painting of hull and installing remaining fittings.

2012 : floating the ship in the wet dock, stepping masts.

2013 : installation of rigging, finishing and fitting out, sea trials.

2014 : training of crew.

2015 : in March-April, or perhaps a little earlier if a miracle occurs, casting off moorings and following La Fayette's route for the inaugural voyage to America !

The duration of the reconstruction

Recovering the skills and know-how of the 18*th* century, adapting the work to conform to modern security regulations and sharing the cultural and technical adventure with the public requires time, hence the apparent slowness of the project. Also, each phase of work is only put in hand once the corresponding budget has been sought and secured. However, going slowly complicates the job technically, because of the excessive drying out of the timbers fitted first. Nonetheless, a veritable feat has been achieved in ensuring that the activity remains constant and the progress steady.

The entire team of shipwrights of the Asselin company happily celebrate the putting in position of the stern frame and the stern-most rib frame in September 1997. Photo François Asselin.

Drums and fifes of the King's Marines. They are always called on for every major festivity in Rochefort. (Photo JMB)

The visitors

Guides show visitors round throughout the year, with an average of 260 000 visits per year, peaking sharply during the summer. Numerous group visits, particularly of school pupils, are organized on request. The association can never thank these visitors enough, as the reconstruction is helped by their enthusiasm and by their purchases from the *Hermione*'s 'souvenir counter'.

A wide range of good quality articles is on sale to the visitors.

The Naopleon III era dock at Rochefort, next to the earlier double dock, will be filled with water and equipped once more with a boat-shaped dock gate in order to harbour the Hermione. *To the left can be seen the yard of the shipwrights building the* Hermione.

Use

The *Hermione*, the replica in the wake of her forebear

The maiden voyage is scheduled to occur in the first months of 2015, taking the ship to the Atlantic coast of America, with visits to Chesapeake Bay and of course Philadelphia, New York, Boston, Baltimore and perhaps the Gulf of Saint Lawrence and Quebec. The original *Hermione* went to all of these places during her tour of duty off the American coast from January 23rd to February 26th 1782.

After her first voyage, she is scheduled to remain at Rochefort or in neighbouring waters for at least nine months every year, which does not preclude trips to nearby ports. But it is intended that she should be often visible at Rochefort, probably afloat in the Napoleon III dock, just next to where she was built. Precautions will be taken against marine parasites, sea-weed and shipworm. As dry docks were only flooded for very short periods, to allow a ship to enter or go out, it is not certain that the Napoleon III dock would withstand being permanently full of water. Tests will be undertaken to verify this.

CREWS OF YESTERDAY AND TODAY

For the American campaign, there was a crew of 316[1], consisting of :
- 14 officers, including the surgeon, the apothecary and the chaplain,
- 44 warrant and petty officers[2], of whom the master gunner, the master carpenter and the master caulker were key men,
- 152 seamen, including 12 topmen and 9 helmsmen,
- 35 non-commissioned officers and marines,
- 71 supernumeraries, surgeons, bakers, armourers, ship's boys, pilot, servants, guards,

The 14 passengers, namely La Fayette and his retinue, brought the total complement to 330 persons.

The modern professional crew will consist of about 30 expert sailors, including 15 from the French navy, helped by the same number of volunteers, experienced and keen amateur sailors. The navigational certification status and the insurance policies do not allow any guests or paying passengers on board, but numerous members of the Hermione association and other supporters will photograph and follow the ship, by sailing in convoy with her during her voyages.

---

[1] According to L'*Hermione, frigate des lumières* by Gireaud and Kalbach, published by Dervy.
[2] 17 for working the ship, 19 for the guns and 8 for the ship's hull and rig (according to Gireaud and Kalbach).

THE *HERMIONE* IN FIGURES

The stages in the life of the ancestor, the *Hermione* of 1779

Late 1778, early 1779 : construction in 5 months, from 15th December 1778 to 12th April 1779.
29th April 1779 :launched, masts shipped on 1st May.
15th May 1779 : admitted into service, descent of the river Charente and putting to sea.
24th May 1779 : first engagement against an enemy privateer in the Gulf of Gascony.
November and December 1779 : return to Rochefort to have her bottom copper sheathed.
20th March 1780 : departure for America with La Fayette, who had come aboard on 10th March.
2nd May 1780 : arrival at Boston, La Fayette leaves the ship.
7th June 1780 : engagement against the British frigate *Iris*, during which the *Hermione* fires 260 shots.
4th May 1781 : reception of the American Congress on board the *Hermione*.
21st July 1781 : battle of Louisburg, the *Hermione* fires 509 cannon shots.
25th February 1782 : return to Rochefort harbour and refit in May-June 1782.
From 1782 to 1784 : tour of duty in India[3] ; in 1789, start of major overhaul.
20 September 1793 : wrecked on the Four Bank off Le Croisic.

The armament of the *Hermione*
26 iron 12-pdr guns – round-shot weight 5.4 kg, diameter 11.6 cm.
6 or 8 6-pdr guns, as well as swivel guns, muskets and pistols.
26 gun-ports with guns, and 2 bow-chaser ports with port-lids, without permanent guns.
Weight of guns : without carriage, a 12-pdr weighs 1.6 tons, a 6-pdr weighs 840 kilos.
All the cannons together weigh 58 tons and their carriages weigh 17 tons. The *Hermione* carried 2040 shot weighing 15 tons and 2.5 tons of gunpowder. The overall weight of the armament is therefore 92.5 tons.

THE RECONSTRUCTED *HERMIONE*

The reconstruction of the hull

Start of construction : in February 1997, draughts and templates made, keel laid on 4th of July 1997.
The dimensions of the *Hermione* : overall length 65 m. Hull 44.20 m x 11.20 m beam x 12 m high. Overall height : 54 m. Total weight : 1 256 tons.
The keel is 44.20 m long and is composed of three vertical layers, each of 4 or 5 trees. False keel at the bottom, outside the planking, with keel and dead-wood above, the latter with cut-outs to take the floor timbers, which are covered by the keelson. Between stem and stern there are 62 ribs.
Around ten different trades are called upon, woodcutters, shipwrights, caulkers, carpenters, wood-carvers, blacksmiths, riggers, sail-makers, painters, etc., not forgetting the historian, the naval architect and the draughtsman. Cost of the project : 17 million euros.

Materials required
Oak for the hull, coming from the forests of the western seaboard of France and softwood for the decks and spars. The coniferous softwood, including Douglas Fir, comes from the hills and mountains in the east of France. The spars are made of glued North American Douglas Fir or spruce.
Crooked oaks are trees deformed by the search for light. Because of the round shape of a ship,

---

[3] See *L'Hermione, frigate des lumières* by Gireaud and Kalbach, published by Dervy.

In 1992, one of the last exploitations of traditional fir trees for masts in the Pyrenees (Issaux), see page 93.

curved pieces of timber are required, cut from wood having the same curve in order to respect the lie of the fibres.
Oak : 1 160 m³, softwood : 205 m³, iron : 35 tons, pitch : 1 ton, oakum ; 3 tons, hemp : 15 tons.

Masts and rigging

Height of masts : 56.55 m for the main-mast, of which 45 m above the deck, 54 m for the fore-mast, both resting on the keel. 35 m for the mizzen mast stepped on the orlop deck.
Bowsprit : 16.25 long, projecting over the stem to hold the mast stays and to carry the jibs.
The main yard, hung square on the main-mast, is 25.5 m long.
The main top : platform to support the upper masts, 5.4 x 5.7, i.e. 30 m².
Sails : 900 to 1 200 m² sail area, made of canvas woven from hemp or flax, heavy and short-lived. The new Hermione will have sails of treated cotton or of synthetic textile, coloured like unbleached canvas.

Information on the site

Visits to the shipyard : every day (except 25th December and 1st January).
Information : Association Hermione-La Fayette, BP 70 177, 17308 Rochefort.
Tel. 05 46 82 07 07 (from outside France : 00 33 5 46 82 07 07)
Internet site : http://www.hermione.com

Glossary
of shipbuilding terms

On the forecastle, inboard from the bulwarks and their projecting kevel-heads, a higher guardrail with metal uprights has been installed for safety reasons. This is not an authentic period fitting. A metal pole with a wooden circle on the end has been placed provisionally where the bowsprit will be. The cut-water is waiting for its lion figurehead (see pages 86, 87and 122). (Photo JMB)

ADZE : one of the main tools of the shipwright, with a curved iron fixed at right-angles to a long handle, for shaping timber.

APRON : curved timber fixed behind lower part of the stem, just above foremost end of the keel.

BACK-STAYS : breast-back-stays to the ship's sides, after-back-stays to the stern ; ropes supporting the upper masts (see page 95)

BARRICADES : rails on quarter-deck, fo'c'sle and waist above the bulwarks with nets to be stuffed with full hammocks before battle to protect the crew from small shot.

BELAYING PIN : ash, lathe-turned pins around which ropes are wound to secure them. The pins are pushed into holes in a rack or other fixing.

BITS : strong perpendicular timbers or frames, particularly on fore-deck, to fasten anchor and other cables.

BLOCK : pulley with its frame or shell. Blocks of many shapes and sizes are disposed on the masts, yards and sails.

BLOCK-STRAP : rope or iron band encircling the block in scores gauged out around the cheeks and fixed to the object worked by the block by means of an eye of rope or an iron hook.

BOLTS : several sorts of iron bolt used in ships, the longest of over 3 m holding the stern post assembly together.

BOTTOM : the part which is under water when the ship is laden.

BOWLINE : rope fastened to the leech or perpendicular edge of square sails, via several bridles, to tauten the weather edge when the sail is close-hauled to a transverse wind.

BOWSPRIT : large boom projecting over the stem, about 36° above the horizontal, to carry sail forward and support the masts by means of the fore-stays running to the head of the fore-mast.

BRACES : main braces, fore-top-gallant braces, etc. Ropes attached to the yard-arms to traverse the sails to the wind direction.

BRAIL : rope for hauling up to the yards the lower corners and skirts of the square sails and for trussing up the mizzen sail.

BREAMING : burning off the filth from a ship's bottom and melting the pitch, then scraping off and applying fresh coat of sulphur and tallow.

BREAST-HOOKS : thick, curved timbers placed horizontally inside the hull across the stem to unite it with the bows on each side.

BREECHING : strong rope harness to secure cannons and limit their recoil.

CABLE : strong rope made of 3 strands, with a standard length of 120 fathoms (about 200 metres) to which the anchor is attached.

CABLE'S LENGTH : measure by which distances between ships in a fleet were usually estimated.

CANT TIMBERS : ribs at both ends of the ship not set at right-angles to the keel to follow the narrowing of the hull to meet the stem and stern posts. Knuckle timbers are the foremost cant timbers on a ship's bow.

CAP : elm block set on top of the mast-head with a hole through which the top-mast is drawn up. (description, photo p 92.)

CAPSTAN : massive timber column, mounted on a spindle, with sockets to receive levers. The crew turn the bars to heave in the anchor cable, lift artillery, etc. There are 2 capstans, the fore on the fo'c'stle and the main on the gun deck abaft the main-mast.

CAREENING : heaving the ship down on one side to expose the bottom on the opposite side for cleaning off fouling by breaming.

CAT-HARPINGS : ropes drawing in the tops of the lower mast shrouds to tighten them and allow the yards to turn obliquely in a side-wind.

CAT-HEADS : short horizontal beams projecting from the bows to suspend the anchor clear of the hull.

CAULKING : making hull planking water-tight by filling the seams between the planks with oakum and covering it with hot melted pitch.

CEILING : the inside planks lining the hull, of various thicknesses according to position. Also called foot-waling.

CHEEKS, OF THE HEAD : lodging knees, usually decorated, fixed to the bow either side of the knee of the head to give lateral support.

CHEEKS, OF THE MAST : projecting pieces on the sides of the masts to support the trestle-trees and the top platform.

CHEEKS, OF BLOCKS : the sides of the shell of a block.

CHEVILLARD : name of the engineer responsible for building the Hermione, completed in the record time of 6 months.

CLAMPS : thick planks inside the hull extending from stem to stern, close under each deck, supporting the ends of the deck beams.

COAT : piece of tarred canvas nailed around the masts where they pass through the deck, the bowsprit where it lies over the stem, the rudder post where it enters the counter through the helm-port, to prevent ingress of water.

COMPASS TIMBER : naturally crooked pieces of timber suitable for shaping into curved frames following the lie of the wood fibre.

CRAIN : Centre de Recherche pour l'Architecture et l'Industrie Nautiques. First project manager for the Hermione reconstruction, responsible for the re-constitution in three dimensions of the frigate's shape.

CRIBBING, BLOCKS : superposed wooden blocks placed at intervals under the keel during construction to raise it to a convenient height for working.

CROSS-PIECE OF BITS : Strong horizontal beam between forward main bits on gun-deck, used for securing anchor. Also stout oak bars athwart the ship's boats below the clamps, enabling them to be lifted with tackle from the yard-arms.

CROSS-TREES : athwart timbers, supported by the cheeks and trestle-trees at the tops of the masts. On the lower mast, they support the frame of the top platform, on the top-mast they spread the top-gallant shrouds.

CROTCH : floor timber with narrow angled fork placed on the keel at the fore and hind ends where the hull curves in tightly.

CUT-WATER : also called knee of the head : foremost part of the ship's prow, formed from several pieces of timber.

DAVIT : piece of timber used as crane to hoist the anchor flooks to the top of the bow without damaging the planking.

DEAD-EYE : round flattish wooden block encircled with a rope or iron band, pierced with three holes for the lanyard lashing the pair of dead-eyes together. The system, acting like multiple pulleys, produces leverage to tension the shrouds. The lower dead-eye is encircled by the iron hoop of the upper link of the shroud chain, the upper one by the spliced end of the shroud.

DEAD-WORKS : the part of a ship which is above the water when she is laden.

DECK-BEAMS : strong timbers with slight dome shape holding together the two sides of the ship and supporting the decks.

DOCK, DRY OR GRAVING : dock fitted with flood-gates, able to be pumped dry, in which ships can be built, repaired or breamed.

FASHION-PIECES : aftmost timbers, terminating the breadth and forming the shape of the stern.

FISH : long piece of wood, convex on one side, concave on the other, used to strengthen damaged masts and yards by woolding.

FLOOR-TIMBERS : timber set across the keel having the futtocks scarphed to it. In 18th century, symmetrical and complemented by cross-chocks, in the 19th century, assymmetrical with long arm facing in alternate directions.

FOOT-HOOK SHROUDS : or futtock shrouds : ropes running from the catharpings to the foot-hook plates, also enabling topmen to climb to the top brim.

FORE-CASTLE, FO'C'SLE : short upper deck reaching from the bows to behind the fore-chains, with breast-work, the fore capstan, carronades.

FORE-FOOT KNEE : timber connecting the fore-end of the keel to the bottom of the stem. Also called 'Gripe'.

FURNITURE : all the fittings, including masts, sails, yards, anchors, cables, helm, artillery, etc.

FURR, FURRING : small piece of the same wood, inserted and glued into timber to replace knot, defective or rotten part.

FUTTOCKS : middle parts of the ribs, the ground or lower futtocks being joined to the floor timbers and cross-chocks, the upper futtocks being joined to the top-timbers.

GARBOARD STREAK : the line of planks laid next to the keel, with their lower edges let into a groove or rabbet in the side of the keel.

GUNS : the Hermione carried 26 x 12-pdr guns on the gun-deck and 6 x 6-pdrs on the quarter-deck and forecastle.

GUN-ROOM : area at after end of gun-deck for storing gun-powder and lodging master gunner on large ships. Officers' quarters in frigates.

HALYARD : rope and tackle to hoist or lower any sail on its mast or stay.

HAMMERING : foresters' method of marking trees designated for felling as marine timber. (see p 44)

HAND-CROW-LEVER : wooden bar with a claw at the end, used by the gun crew for manoeuvering the artillery

HAND-SPIKE : wooden bar used as a lever for the windlass, stowing cargo in the hold, moving archors, etc

HAWSE-HOLES : holes in the bows on either side of the stem for the passage of the anchor cables or chains.

HEAD : ornamental figure on the top of the stem, emblematic of the ship's name or purpose - war, commerce, etc.

HEAD : structure ahead of the bows, supporting the bowsprit, decorated with figure and other carved and painted elements.

HEADS : gratings on either side of the stem serving as latrines for the sailors.

HEART : form of dead-eye, heart-shaped, with a single hole in the middle, mainly used for tensioning stays.

HEAVE DOWN : pulling on the masts to heel the ship over to expose one side of her bottom for careening.

HELM-PORT : hole in the counter through which the top of the rudder post passes, with coat to prevent entry of water.

HORSE : rope parallel to the yard 1 metre below it as a foothold for the topmen when they are loosing, reefing or furling the sails.

JEARS : tackles for hoisting up (swaying) and lowering (striking) the lower yards to their position on the mast.

JIB : jib, flying jib, fore-stay sail, fore-topmast-stay sail, etc. Fore-and-aft sails rigged between the fore-mast and the bowsprit.

KEEL : fundamental timber of a ship, first element to be laid, prolonged by stem and stern-post elevated on its ends. Keels of more than 12 to 15 m are composed of several timbers scarphed together. Dead-wood, notched to take the floor timbers, is placed on the keel and the assembly is topped by the keelson. Rabbets cut in the sides of the keel take the edges of the garboard

KEELSON : scarphed timbers forming a counter-keel, sandwiching the floor timbers and crotches against the keel with long copper bolts.

KEVEL : forked frames fixed to ship's side, their arms serving to belay the sheets of the main-sail and fore-sail.

KEVEL-HEAD : extensions of top timbers rising above the forecastle bulwarks, used to belay large ropes and cables.

KNEES : crooked pieces of timber with two arms forming greater or smaller angle according to the pieces they unite. Knees may be 'hanging' (vertical), 'lodging' (horizontal), 'dagger' (oblique) or 'standard' (against the vertical side of deck-beams, different from those simply called 'standards', see that entry). Greatly strengthen the frame. Often reinforced by iron brackets, as on the *Hermione*, and later replaced by cast iron knees, owing to the rarity of suitable timber. French 'genou' is not a knee, but a lower futtock. The stern-post knee, joining the aft end of the keel to the stern-post, is one of the largest knees in a ship.

KNIGHT-HEAD : strong posts containing several sheaves for the lower jears, situated just forward of the capstans on forecastle and gun-deck. Originally embellished with carved figure of human head.

KNIGHT-HEADS : strong timbers either side of stem rising high enough to secure the bowsprit.

LANYARD : short rope or line mainly used to lash pairs of dead-eyes together, acting like tackle to apply force to tauten the rigging.

LARBOARD : the old term for 'port', the left hand side of a ship looking forward.

LIFTS : ropes from the mast-head cap to the yard-arms, to support the weight of the yard, particularly with topmen working, and to adjust its horizontality and to pull one extremity higher than the other when required.

LIGNUM VITAE : gaiacum, cocus, green-heart : exotic woods from the West Indies, very hard wearing with lubricating properties, used for pins and sheaves of blocks and for dead-eyes.

MASTS : frigates and ships of the line always had 3 masts, each composed of lower mast, top-mast, top-gallant-mast. (see pp 91-93)

MIDSHIP BEAM : the longest deck-beam, fixed to the midship frame, serving as the standard for dimensions of masts and yards.

MODEL : at a time when draughts were not used, extremely accurate scale models were produced for the dockyards, each component being an exact reduced scale replica of the original to enable the shipwrights to visualize the piece they were to shape. The 1/18th scale working model of the Hermione has been made in front of project visitors by the cabinet-maker Jean Thomas.

PARRAL : collar composed of ribs and trucks to attach the top-sail yards to the masts and allowing the yards to slide up and down.

QUARTER-DECK : upper deck reaching from the stern to the waist, site of the helm and command post, carrying light guns, usually carronades.

QUARTER-GALLERY : lateral projection from each quarter of the stern, with carved decoration, fitted up as conveniences for the officers. See 'Heads'.

PARTNER : frame fitted in the apertures of the decks where the masts pass through, to strengthen the decks and protect them from the pressure of the masts. Similarly for the bowsprit, rudder-post and pumps. Fitted with water-proof coats (see 'coats' entry).

PLANKS, PLANKING : strong boards covering and lining the sides of the hull, making it water-tight. The thicker planks of the main-, channel- and gun-wales reinforce the structure, as do the internal thick-stuff and clamps. Planking of war-ships was mostly of oak, with a limited use of beech. Upper-works and top decks were of pine for lightness. Planks were bent to shape with steam.

PITCH : Resinous substance, produced by boiling down tar, used in caulking the chinks between the planks of decks and hulls.

PORTS : openings in the ship's side to enable the guns to be run out for action. In certain cases fitted with port-lids.

PORT-LID : doors hung from hinges on their upper edges, closed with guns run in to prevent rough seas entering the gun deck.

RABBET : groove cut with an adze in the sides of the keel, stem and stern-post to receive the edges and ends of the hull planking.

RACK : frame of timber containing several sheaves and holes for belaying pins, situated on forecastle and quarter-deck.

RAILS OF THE HEAD : curved wooden pieces running obliquely from the bows below the cat-heads to support the knee of the head.

RATLINES (RATLINGS) : small lines strung horizontally accros the shrouds to provide ladders for the topmen to go aloft.

REEF, TO : reduce (shorten) surface of sails by taking in one or more reefs, with points, flat braided cords to be threaded through eyelets.

RIBS : also called frames or timbers. Attached to the keel like animal's ribs to the spine, the ribs make the structure and shape of the ship and the hull planking is fixed to them. They are composed of scarphed futtocks ; 2 assmblies laid side by side with off-set joins are bolted together. The midship frame is the largest. The principal timbers are the major frames fitted first and serving as guides for the intermediate ribs. Filling timbers are inserted between the ribs to strengthen the structure and to impede penetration by cannon balls. (see pp 64-69)

RIBAND : long, narrow, flexible pieces of wood nailed to the outside of the ribs, running lengthways along the hull. Their interior surface will determine the curve of the intermediate timbers. They allow the form of the hull to be visualized before the planks are laid.

RIG, TO : to fit all the standing and running rigging to a ship

RIGGING : general name for all the ropes used to support the masts, extend or reduce the sails or dispose them to suit the wind.

RIGGING, RUNNING : ropes for arranging the sails, braces, sheets, clew-lines, halyards, etc, often passing through blocks.

RIGGING, STANDING : employed to support the masts and remaining in fixed position : shrouds, stays and back-stays.

RISING LINE : curved line drawn on sheer-draughts to determine the height of the ends of the floor timbers, hence the profile of the hull.

ROPES : many types and sizes made in rope factories or alleys. Standard length cables about 200 m long. (see pp 100-101)

RUDDER : means of steering attached to the stern-post by pintles and braces. (see pp 116-117)

SAPWOOD : the most recent growths of wood, proscribed for ship-building, which only used hardened heartwood.

SCANTLING : standardized breadths and thicknesses of timbers for each type of ship.

SCARPHED JOINT : joining timbers end to end with a tapered joint, as opposed to a butt joint, cut square.

SHEATHING : covering nailed all over a ship's bottom to protect the hull from ship-worm. Fir planks were first used, then large headed iron nails, lastly sheets of copper fastened on with sheathing nails. Coppering greatly increased the speed of vessels and besides protection against worm also prevented weed and barnacles from adhering. The Hermione, coppered in December 1779, was one of the first French ships to benefit from this treatment.

SHEAVE : wheel, usually made of lignum-vitae or brass, on which the rope works in a block.

SHEET : rope attached to lower corner of sail to spread and hold it to leeward; used with a tack in side winds, in pairs with stern-wind.

SHIP OF THE LINE : all men-of-war large and powerful enough to be placed in the line of battle. Normally carrying at least 60 guns.

SHORES : props fixed under a ship's wales to support her whilst building.

SHROUD CHAIN : chains fixed to the ship's sides, passing through the chain-wales, the upper link encircling the lower dead-eye of the shroud.

SHROUDS : part of the standing rigging ; large ropes from the mast-heads to chain-wales on the sides of the ship to give lateral support to the masts. Tautened by lanyards lashed between pairs of dead-eyes.

STANCHION : removable pillar supporting the deck-beams (see p 81).

STANCHION : various smaller posts on the deck for the netting, quarter-rails, etc, fixed to the gun-wale or on the top platform supporting the safety net for the topmen (see p 96).

STANDARD : inverted vertical knee placed above the deck rather than beneath it (hanging knee), with the vertical branch pointing upwards.

STANDARD OF THE HEAD : inverted vertical knee fastening the cut-water to the stem, hook shaped at the top for attaching the mast stays.

STARBOARD : the right side of the ship when facing forwards. Originally 'steerboard' when ships had an oar or sweep lashed to the side for steering before rudders were adopted. The 'noble' side on which officers come aboard.

STAYS : large strong ropes from the mast-heads running foreward, providing support for the masts. The fore-stay and fore-topmast stay run to the end of the bowsprit, the main-stay to the head standard. The mizzen stays are fixed to the main-mast. They are tensioned by means of lanyards lashed through 'hearts', similar to dead-eyes but with a single large hole.

STAY-SAILS : triangular sails extended on stay-sail stays.

STEM : timber joined to the fore end of the keel via the fore-foot knee and having the bowsprit resting on the upper end. The planks of the hull are rabbetted into it.

STEP : block of oak forming a socket for seating the heel of the mast. Those of the fore and main masts are fixed to the keelson, that of the mizzen mast is fixed to the orlop deck, as is the step for the main capstan spindle.

STERN FRAME : frame comprising the stern-post, transoms and fashion-pieces.

STERN-POST : long straight timber rising from the aft end of the keel and fixed to it by a massive knee. The ends of all the lower planks of the ship's bottom fit into rabbets in its sides. The stern-frame is fixed to it and it bears the entire weight and force of the rudder.

STIRRUPS : short ropes hanging down from the yards with eyes at their lower ends though which the horses are reeved (see 'Horse').

STRAKE OR STREAK : range of planks running from the stem to the stern-post.

STRING : highest range of planks in the ceiling, between the gun-whale and the upper edge of the upper deck ports.

SWAYING UP : hoisting the lower yards and upper masts into position. The latter slide through the hole in the lower mast cap and were lowered out of harm's way when the ship was inactive. (see p 92)

TACK : rope to draw forward the leading corner of a square or stay sail in a side-wind and to hold it to windward.

TACKLE : a block with its associated rope.

TAR : liquid gum from conifers used for preserving wood and ropes, the latter being boiled in tar-kettles.

TEMPLATE : pattern made of thin pine or plywood cut to exact shape of timber to be formed.

TOP : platform surrounding the lower mast-head, with main function of providing a wide base for the top-mast shrouds. (see p 96)

TOP-MAN : seaman designated for work aloft.

TOPSAIL-SHEET BIT : for belaying smaller ropes, notably the topsail sheets.

TRANSOMS : beams fixed across the stern-post. Deck-transom, aftmost beam of gun-deck, has deck planks rabbetted into it.

TRANSOM, WING : topmost transom in stern-frame with complex dual curve, vertical 'round-up' and horizontal 'round-aft'.

TREE-NAIL : large oak cylindrical peg about 3 cm in diameter for fastening the planking to the frame or holding together the side by side thicknesses of the ribs. Sometimes cleft ended to have a quoin driven in. (see p 76)

TRESTLE-TREES : oak bars fixed on the hounds of the lower masts to support the cross-trees and the weight of the top-mast.

TRUCKS : wheels of gun-carriages, made of elm (see p 108). Also spacer beads, made of ash, between ribs of parrals (see that entry).

TUMBLEHOME : curve in ship's upper-works, making ship gradually narrower from the lower deck upwards.

WALES : strakes of thicker outer planks along the whole length of the ship's side. Main-wale, level with the gun-deck, strengthens that deck. Channel-wale serves same purpose for upper gun-deck on ships of the line. Gun-wale or gunnel is smaller wale at level of quarter-deck.

WOOD-GRAIN : the lie of the fibres in wood ; to obtain maximum strength the direction of the grain must always be respected.

WOOLD : to wind rope around a mast or yard to support it in a place where it has been fished or scarphed.

YARD : long horizontal timber suspended from the masts to carry the square sails..

Bibliography

The following few bibliographical references only indicate currently available modern works concerning the Hermione, wooden sailing ships and forestry exploitation. It is by no means an exhaustive list.

By the same author and publisher
Bois de marine, 2000.
Bois de musique, 2003.
250 réponses aux questions des amoureux de la forêt, 2006.

Dictionaries
LECOMTE, Jules : *Dictionnaire pittoresque de marine*, Chasse-marée éditions de l'Estran, 1835 new edition 1998.
WILLAUMEZ, Admiral : *Dictionnaire de marine*, Mame, 1831 new edition 1998.

Naval
BAYLE, Luc-Marie, and MORDAL, Jacques : *La marine en bois*, Fayard, 1978.
BOUDRIOT, Jean : *Artillerie de mer, France 1650-1850*, Archéologie navale, 1992.
COSSÉ, Yves : *Les frères Crucy, entrepreneurs de constructions navales de guerre, 1793-1814*, Y.C., 1993.
Neptunia, Revue des amis du Musée national de la Marine, 1946 to the present.

War of American Independence, American Revolutionary War
FORRAY, Gilbert, général : *La route de Yorktown*, conference given at the Sorbonne, 2003.
GIRAULT DE COURSAC, Pierrette and Paul, *Guerre d'Amérique et liberté des mers*, mairie de Paris, 1983.

Hermione
FONTAINIEU, Emmanuel de : *L'Hermione, de Rochefort à la gloire américaine*, Éditions de Monza, 1992.
KALBACH, Robert and GIREAUD, Jean-Luc: *L'Hermione, frégate des lumières*, Dervy, 2004.

Wood
GAY, collective work with contributions by J.-M. BALLU : *L'Atlas du bois*, Éditions de Monza, 2001.

La Fayette's departure on April 20th 1777 aboard the Victoire for his first voyage to America: painting by Hubert Robert. Musée national de la coopération franco-américaine at Blérancourt, detail. © R.M.N., Gérard Blot.